A CENTURY AIRBORNE

AIR TRAILS OF PEARSON AIRPARK

By

Jon Walker

Rose Wind

Vancouver, Washington

I.S.B.N.: 0-9631232-2-X
Walker, Jon
A CENTURY AIRBORNE
Bibliography: p. 99
Includes index: p. 101

Cover design by Mary Rose
Title Page photo of Alexander Pearson (National Archives)

TABLE OF CONTENTS

FOREWORD

It is about time that someone wrote a history of Pearson Field worthy of the role the airstrip has played in the history of aviation. Jon Walker has finally done it. He has written the comprehensive, authoritative story of the airfield from Lincoln Beachey to Valeri Chkalov and beyond.

His book should end all arguments about the historical significance of this last of the Army airfields of World War I. Walker does not attempt to determine whether Pearson Air Park is the oldest continuously operating airfield in the country, older than College Park, Maryland. Pearson's colorful history speaks for itself.

Walker spent three years in research and interviews for the book while working for a master's degree in history at Portland State University. He served as curator of the Air Museum on Pearson Field from 1989 through 1991.

His book, edited by Mary Rose and published by Rose Wind Press, is more than a recital of dates and events. There was something about the open field in Vancouver Barracks and the adjoining bottom land that attracted men with the look of eagles in their eyes.

When Lincoln Beachey, the boy aviator, took off from the Lewis and Clark Exposition grounds in his primitive dirigible in 1905 he headed for the wide open polo and artillery grounds, delivering a letter from Portland's mayor, Dr. Harry Lane (a dentist) to Vancouver's mayor, E.G. Crawford. The excitement he generated seemed to inspire men like Silas Christofferson to build and fly pusher planes like the Wright Brothers' Fliers. Si put Vancouver in the headlines when he flew off the roof of the Multnomah Hotel, June 12, 1912, and landed on the site of what is now Pearson Air Park.

Walter Edwards helped put Vancouver on the navigator's chart when he flew the first official interstate airmail from Portland to the polo grounds August 10, 1912.

The field was also the birthplace of a lot of planes that didn't fly. Allen Manning built a plane in a barn in Fruit Valley and hired Charles Walsh to fly it. It never got off the ground. Neither did Emil Komm's home built plane, a monoplane like Louis Bleriot's. It was towed behind an auto at the barracks but never flew. The *Student Prince*, built and flown at the airfield by Aircraft Builders, Inc., however, proved to be a commercial success.

The book is well written, thoroughly researched and spiced with tidbits, such as the mystery of the $100 bills found in the bedroom of General George C. Marshall's house where the Russian polar fliers slept after their historic flight across the North Pole.

And there is a story of the mule that stuck his head into the tent housing one of those early experimental airplanes. The planes were kept on the artillery drill grounds where the army pastured its mules. One mule managed to get his head stuck in the tail wires of a Bleriot monoplane.

Walker emphasizes the role of the spruce mill built with wartime urgency and operated by the army on the airfield during World War I. The mill was the major source of spruce for construction of the wood and linen airplanes for the war effort. The Spruce Corporation was the city's first real industry, Walker notes.

Walker points out that the historic old airport has played a major role in peace and war. How much longer it will survive depends on the fate of legislation that includes Pearson Air Park in an Historic Reserve along with Officers' Row and the Fort Vancouver Historic Site.

Leverett Richards
*Retired Aviation and Military
Editor of* The Oregonian, *who
learned to fly at Pearson in 1938*

INTRODUCTION

The development of controlled manned-flight has had a tremendous effect on transportation. It has dramatically reduced travel time, making long distance travel convenient and efficient. This has affected business, communication, response to emergencies, family relations, and the nature of war. Manned-flight has diminished the effect of distance and changed people's perception of it. The realization of this long-time dream of humankind ranks among the greatest and farthest reaching technological innovations in history.

Controlled flight progressed rapidly after the turn-of-the-century. Though the Wright brothers first flew an airplane in 1903, it wasn't until 1908 that the general public took heavier-than-air flight seriously. Lighter-than-air flight, however, using hydrogen gas, was widely accepted. During the nineteenth century free-flight ballooning became a major spectator event in America. Balloons were used for military reconnaissance during the Civil War. Shortly after the Civil War free-flight ballooning started to lose its novelty and public interest began to wane. Around the turn-of-the-century controlled, powered flight was being tried with some success. Most of this was in dirigible balloons.

An aerial contest was held at the St. Louis Louisiana Purchase Exposition of 1904. The St. Louis exposition was the first major exhibition of controlled flight in the United States. All of the flying at the exposition was done in lighter-than-air craft (the Wrights chose not to compete because they believed the contest rules discriminated against their airplane). The following year Lincoln Beachey made 23 successful flights at a similar exposition in Portland, Oregon (the Lewis and Clark Centennial Exposition). Over the next three years, aeronauts such as Beachey, Roy Knabenshue, and Charles Hamilton toured extensively in the United States and abroad with dirigibles.

Successful flights by the Wrights (Wilbur in Europe, Orville for the Army at Ft. Meyer, Virginia) and Glenn Curtiss in 1908 effectively introduced the public to the airplane. By the time Louis Bleriot flew across the English Channel in 1909 most people were convinced of the reality, though not the practicality, of heavier-than-air flight.

The Wrights, with great accuracy, predicted a possible progression of aviation. It would start with "military reconnaissance, . . . then exploration, speedy transportation of passengers and freight, including mail, and finally for sport." Their prediction pointed to the need to make the airplane more reliable and to produce them in large numbers. The period between 1910 and the end of World War I was primarily focused on these two tasks.

Exhibition fliers not only thrilled crowds, but also tested the limits of airplane and pilot. The war forced the United States to mass produce airplanes. The Curtiss JN-4 (or *Jenny*) an American aircraft, and the DeHavilland DH-4, an American-made British plane were manufactured in large numbers. Both of these planes were used for barnstorming and early commercial activities, such as air mail, as well as for training thousands of pilots, both military and civilian.

From World War I until the mid-1920's, much of the flying in the United States was done by the struggling Army Air Service. Nearly all the leading aviators were military men. The first non-stop transcontinental flight (1923), the first around-the-world flight (1924), and similar feats were accomplished by Army and Navy pilots under the official auspices of the military.

The letting of commercial air mail contracts in 1925 by the government signaled the start of a new era in aviation. Air mail provided commercial concerns a steady income to develop other parts of the fledgling aviation business (e.g. passenger service, flight training for their employees and others, the construction of new types of non-military airplanes) and a motivation to use and improve the limited airways the Army had developed. The promise of commercial aviation also gave local governments a reason to construct landing fields and airports.

When Charles Lindbergh, a young civilian air mail pilot, made the first solo crossing of the Atlantic in 1927, it caught the American public's imagination. Air mail and passenger business increased dramatically following his ocean hop. The romance surrounding Lindbergh's accomplishment (ironically) helped convince the American public of the practicality of aviation, though only a relatively small portion of the population had actually flown in an airplane and far fewer had piloted one. It remained for technological innovations (especially increases in carrying capacity and passenger comfort) to make travel by air the common, everyday activity that it is today.

Pearson Airpark is a general aviation airport located in Vancouver, Washington. Its development has mirrored much of the general development of aviation in the United States. It had a taste of lighter-than-air controlled flight when Beachey flew to Vancouver Barracks to deliver a message to General Constant Williams in 1905.

Only a year after the area's first heavier-than-air flight (1910, in Portland) experimental aviators began congregating on the barracks flats to try their hand at flying. It had been just three years since the Wrights and Glenn Curtiss had convinced most of the public of the reality, though not the practicality, of heavier-than-air flight.

Various civilian aviators tried their hand at flying at the "polo grounds," so-called because of the army's polo field on the flats. During World War I the army participated in the mass production of aircraft by building and operating the largest cut-up mill in the world on the barracks flats. The establishment of an Army field at the barracks was an early part of the Air Service's program of expansion. Army fields like the one at Vancouver were the backbone of the Air Service, providing intermediate landing sites and places for reserve training. Reserves provided a pool of pilots and mechanics for the Army in case of emergency, and provided many qualified people for the nascent commercial aviation industry. Pearson Field served as a reserve training center until 1941 when members of the 321st Observation Squadron were called to active duty.

The local Chamber of Commerce established a commercial field adjacent to the Army field in 1925. The city of Vancouver took over the operation in 1928. The commercial field was merged with the former Army field following World War II. Since World War II the field has served general aviation purposes: passenger and business flying, pilot instruction, sightseeing flights, and aerial reconnaissance for mapping, photography, and business purposes. The U.S. Army retains avigation rights to the field. After the devastating eruption of Mt. St. Helens in 1980 the Department of the Interior used Pearson Airpark as a base for its aerial operations over the mountain.

Pearson Airpark, and the small to medium-sized fields like it, have played a crucial role in the development of aviation. These fields have helped make flying a widespread, everyday activity. The development of practical airways relied on the existence of these intermediate landing sites. Aviation grew and flourished because of the availability of these fields across the country. The presence of airfields in small towns such as Vancouver also made it possible for the public to see and experience flying first-hand. This in turn made aviation more accepted as a practical and useful endeavor. Public acceptance is necessary to make an endeavor profitable, and profitability is needed to encourage improvements and innovations. This progress in aviation has revolutionized transportation, making it faster, more efficient, and farther reaching. The dramatic reductions in travel time have altered people's perception of distance and changed the world.

ACKNOWLEDGEMENTS

This project began when I became the curator of the Pearson Air Museum in 1989. My qualifications for the job, such as they were, had nothing to do with any particular interest or expertise relating to aviation. My background was in history and museums. Consequently the way the volunteers and members of the museum were mesmerized by flying machines mystified me. In the two years I was at the museum I learned a great deal about aviation and why these people loved flying so much. It was a truly dedicated group of people who wanted to save an historic airport. Pearson Airpark is a piece of history that might well have been lost without their efforts and this book would never have been written without their inspiration.

Dozens of people deserve to be mentioned for their work on behalf of Pearson Airpark. But one who must be mentioned is John Wulle, one of the founders of the Pearson Airpark Historical Society. In his single-minded pursuit of the airport's preservation John has been both endearing and contentious, occasionally at the same time.

The burden of preparing the manuscript was significantly eased by three people. Leverett Richards read a draft and offered helpful suggestions as well as writing the biographies that appear in this book. Vancouver's most respected local historian, Ted Van Arsdol, was kind enough to read a draft and his advice, both comprehensive and detailed, was invaluable. I am indebted to my publisher, Mary Rose, for her patience and generosity in making this project possible. Finally I want to thank my parents . . . for everything.

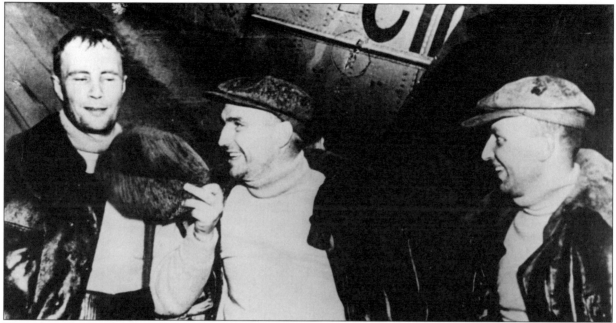

Three weary Russian flyers: Belyakov, Chkalov and Baidukov

World-renowned ANT-25 at Vancouver, WA, June 20,1937

CHAPTER I

THE TRANSPOLAR BRIDGE
"That Plane Is Here"

Early on Sunday morning, newspaperman Erwin Rieger got a phone call he really did not expect. "This is Reynolds. That plane has landed." "That plane," with its three-man Soviet crew, had just made the first non-stop flight over the North Pole and landed at the army's Pearson Field in Vancouver, Washington. The *Columbian's* Rieger called the Associated Press. He had just scooped the whole world.

Neither Rieger nor Lieutenant H. A. "Pat" Reynolds nor anyone else had expected the unprecedented flight to end in Vancouver. Reynolds, the assistant to field commander Major Paul Burrows, was busy posting guards, finding mechanics, and informing General George C. Marshall, the post commandant, that the Russians had landed. But he found time to make good his promise to Rieger to call him if the plane the world was following should land at Pearson.

The crew was composed of three of the Soviet Union's top airmen: Valery Chkalov, pilot, Georgiy Baidukov, co-pilot and instrument pilot, and Alexander Belyakov, navigator. Landing at Pearson on June 20, 1937, the fliers had completed a flight so dangerous that many had thought it was impossible. There was the freezing weather, the arctic storms, and the constant battle against deadly ice forming on the aircraft's wings. The pole's magnetic fields made a compass useless. Navigator Belyakov was skilled in celestial navigation but that would be of little use if clouds obscured the

heavens. A forced landing would be almost certain death for the aviators. The frozen wastes of the arctic and the wilds of northern Canada made rescue a very unlikely proposition. The airmen's landing at Pearson had proved the trip was not impossible, just incredible.

The Soviet Union had long been pursuing cold-weather and long-distance flights. It was, perhaps, the monumental difficulty and accompanying potential for embarrassing failure of the hazardous pole-crossing which caused Soviet authorities to remain quiet about this effort. It was known that the Soviets had landed four planes at the Pole in May and the State Department disclosed that it had given permission for a Soviet aviator to fly over U.S. territory. Still, the Soviet authorities refused to confirm stories about a planned transpolar flight. As late as the evening of June 18th Moscow said it was "unaware" of any such attempt. It fell to the Royal Canadian Signal Corps station at Edmonton, Alberta, to report that a plane had left Moscow at 5:05 p.m. Pacific Daylight Time on June 17, 1937. The Soviets' aerial assault on the pole was now front page news.

Newspapers informed their readers of what they could find out about the airmen and their flight. The intended destination was Oakland, California, approximately 6,000 miles from their take-off point at Schelkovo Aerodrome near Moscow. All three were experienced aviators. They had made a 5,858 mile flight over the desolate arctic reaches of Siberia, landing on the tiny off-shore island of Udd the previous year (1936). Each of the fliers had been awarded the title "Hero of the Soviet Union" for this flight. Still, they didn't get credit for breaking the long-distance record set by French fliers Paul Codos and Maurice Rossi on their 1933 flight from New York to Syria (5,637 nautical miles). The Udd Island flight had not been validated by the Federation Aeronautique Internationale, the international body which oversaw aviation records. This time they hoped to receive that recognition in addition to blazing a path over the pole.

Their plane was a "giant" monoplane with red wings and a gray fuselage. It was a Russian-built type ANT 25, powered by a single 12-cylinder, water-cooled, v-type engine. Its wings spread 112 feet. Two-thousand gallons of fuel were on board, enough for about 100 hours of flying. The largest of the four-motored Clipper flying boats, readers were reminded, carried only 2,400 gallons on their trans-Pacific journeys. The ship was reputed to weigh 24,750 pounds fully loaded with 13,760 pounds of the total being fuel and oil. Even the crew's combined weight, 528 pounds, was reported.

News from the plane's 20-watt radio transmitter was sporadic. The first message, eighteen hours after take-off, said, "We are three hours from the pole, flying nicely." The simple message belied the conditions the fliers were facing. Cyclones met them in the arctic. Ice formed almost five inches thick on the leading edges of the wings. Head winds consumed precious fuel. Temperatures dipped down to 25 degrees below zero Fahrenheit. The men smoked constantly, but ate little. The North Pole passed without fanfare. Belyakov sent a message: "we have crossed the pole — a tail wind — white ice fields with crevices and expanses of open water — our mood is cheerful." To the west another cyclone appeared. Fortunately this one paralleled their path.

They had entered what they called "the pole of inaccessibility," the region between the pole and

Canada. There were no radio beams to guide them. They couldn't receive signals from their comrades in the Soviet Union, nor yet, from the U.S. Coast Guard. And the weather was the worst they faced on the journey. Cyclones and huge banks of clouds rose up 20,000 feet. The ANT-25's maximum ceiling was 18,500 feet. The clouds caused severe icing.

The plane trembled with the stress of the ice while Baidukov flew on instruments. With a thick layer of ice changing the wing loading dangerously, he lowered the engine speed to reduce altitude. Reaching 10,000 feet he increased engine revs to return to level flight. The smell of alcohol signalled a disaster. Somewhere there was a leak in the cooling system. In a few minutes the engine would seize up and quit running. The crew frantically searched for a source of water to feed the cooling system. The drinking water yielded little; it was mostly frozen. In a flash, Baidukov called for the "balloons." The liquid they contained revived the cooling system, but there would be no urine samples for the doctors back home.

On Saturday afternoon, June 19th, the fliers reported their position 100 miles south of Fort Norman, North West Territories. They were about 1000 miles north of the US-Canadian border and heading for the Pacific Coast. In the cockpit the rigors of the Arctic were replaced by concern over how much fuel had been used fighting head winds and avoiding cyclones. Having crossed the pole they had completed their official mission. They might have landed in Canada and still have been the first to fly non-stop over the North Pole. But they were determined to reach San Francisco, which would set a new record for a non-stop flight. A little after 9 p.m. they were over the Queen Charlotte Islands off British Columbia and reported "Everything going well."

Early Sunday morning the crew reported that they might land between Seattle and San Francisco because of diminishing fuel supplies. They requested the radio beam from the Bellingham, Washington air commerce station. Meanwhile,

After the transpolar flight on the steps of the commanding officer's home at Vancouver Barracks, now the Marshall House. (l-r) General George C. Marshall, Georgi Baidukov, Alexander Belyakov, Molly Brown (General Marshall's stepdaughter), Katherine Brown Marshall, Soviet Ambassador A.A. Troyanovsky, Valery Chkalov.

The Soviets' landing at Vancouver rocked the nation with headline news.

FIRST IN INDIANA
In Morning and Sunday Circulation.
Telephone Riley 7311.

THE INDIANAPOLIS STAR

FORECAST FOR TODAY:
Local Showers.
Yesterday's High, 89; Low, 64.

VOL. 35. NO. 16.   MONDAY MORNING, JUNE 21, 1937.   Entered as Second-Class Matter at Post Office, Indianapolis, Ind. Issued Daily and Sunday.   THREE CENTS.

POLAR AIR-TRAIL BLAZERS LAND IN U. S.

Kiwanians Throng City; Sessions Open Today

FAIL TO REACH OAKLAND GOAL BY 580 MILES

7,000 ATTEND MUSIC EVENT, HEAR LEADERS

Townsend, Kern Address Delegates — Callen Will Head International's 21st Conclave.

TODAY'S PROGRAM.

Registration—Murat Temple, all day.

Opening Convention Session—Murat Temple, 9:15 a. m.

International Council Luncheon—Lincoln room, Hotel Lincoln, noon.

District Secretaries' Luncheon and Conference—Parlor E, Hotel Lincoln, noon.

Lieutenant Governors' Conference—Hotel Severin roof gar-

STEEL SHOWDOWN IS TAKING SHAPE

Chicago, June 20.—(P)—Now that George Kiepura, 17 years old, of Phoenix, Ill., has been graduated from high school, he is ready to start his vacation.

Father, Two Sons Rescued, Revived After Speedboat Upsets in River

A father and his two sons, almost drowned when a speedboat in which they were riding upset in White river at 67th street yesterday afternoon, were revived by volunteer first-aid workers and sent to Methodist Hospital, where the condition of none was regarded as serious.

The speedboat, operated by Charles J. Allison, 416 East 24th street, apparently struck some debris in the high waters of the river and overturned. Allison said that when he came up he saw David Morton, 37 years old, 2358 Stuart street, and his son, Edward, 5, another son, William Morton, 8, was out of sight.

Allison dove to the bottom and brought William to the shore. Mr. Morton and Edward were rescued

from the overturned boat by Cecil Scott, city fire captain, who lives near the scene; Lloyd Pearson of Ravenswood, and Loren Sims, 47 West 28th street.

Morton and his two sons, who were unconscious when brought to the bank, were given artificial respiration by Arthur E. Wilson, 28 South Ritter avenue, a Red Cross lifeguard; Scott, Pearson and Sims. None of the three who were in danger could swim.

Jail Calls High School Graduate on 'Vacation'

FIVE KILLED, THREE HURT IN ACCIDENTS

Local Couple, Girl Die as Auto Plunges in River— Tragedies Claim Two at Evansville.

[Special to The Indianapolis Star.]

Seymour, Ind., June 20.—An Indianapolis man, his wife and their adopted daughter met death today when their automobile hurtled off a bridge over White river on United States 31 into 17 feet of water.

The victims:

Edgar O. Milburn, 37.

Maude A. Milburn, 31, his wife.

Mary Frances, 3, the adopted daughter.

Deputy Coroner S. E. Tower

Kiwanians All Smiles as They Await Convention.

They are all smiles as they wait for the 21st annual convention of the Kiwanis International to open today. Left to right, F. Trafford Taylor, St. Boniface, Manitoba, Canada, a vice-president of the organization; Harper Gatton of Madisonville, Ky., immediate past president, and James M. Lynch of Florence, S. C., another vice-president.

Win Through Arctic Perils to Be Grounded by Fog —Up 63 Hours and 17 Minutes.

Vancouver, Wash., June 20.—(P)—Three Russian air heroes blazed a nonstop sky trail from Moscow over the north pole to the United States and landed unheralded here today, forced down by murky weather 580 miles short of Oakland, Cal., goal of their planned 6,000-mile flight.

The huge winged monoplane glided to a perfect landing at Pearson field at 8:22 a. m. (10:22 a. m. Central standard time). The plane and its weary crew had been in the air 63 hours and 17 minutes, when poor visibility brought them to earth.

Tonight, after a day of refreshing sleep, the trio arose long enough to participate in a broadcast in which they gave a world-wide audience brief details of their epic accomplishment. They indi-

newsmen began to gather at the larger airports, including Portland's Swan Island. In Seattle a group of newsmen went aloft in a United Air Lines plane to search for the Soviets without success. At 6 a.m. the crew radioed that clouds were making navigation difficult and asked for the Portland beam. Weather reports showed the ceiling to be at 800 feet in Portland.

South of Portland, near Eugene, Oregon, the fliers became alarmed when fuel pressure began to drop abruptly. They did not know what sort of conditions might await them further south. They agreed to return to Portland where they had observed weather conditions. At 8 a.m. a message was received: "Pump does not work — will land in Portland." Hundreds of aviation buffs and newsmen jammed the Swan Island Airport in that city.

Baidukov, at the controls, picked his way through the clouds and fog to find the Columbia River. But, on locating Swan Island, Chkalov waved him off. "Too many people" he said, "They'll take our plane apart for souvenirs." "The military airport in Vancouver," said Chkalov holding a map in Baidukov's face, "is where we will land."

Leaving the disappointed throng in Portland, the fliers crossed the Columbia River and made a pass over Pearson Field. Their glider-like plane, nearly emptied of fuel, was light and would be difficult to land, especially as it had no brakes nor flaps. But the wet field would help slow the plane.

Baidukov lined up on the west end of the field and skillfully managed to get the plane to "set down." As they rolled along the soggy field the plane jumped. Startled, Chkalov asked what it was. A crosswalk, replied Baidukov. (It was East Reserve Street, and the bounce the aircraft experienced was typical for planes that made a long landing roll.) The field was almost deserted. It was 8:22 a.m., they had been in the air nearly 63 hours.

Chkalov climbed out of the plane while Baidukov and Belyakov worked inside. The commander was surprised to be greeted in Russian by George Kozmetsky, a University of Washington R.O.T.C. student who happened to be walking by at the time. Kozmetsky later related that the fliers "were all business." Chkalov asked for wheel chocks and, after securing the plane, a telephone or telegraph. But the world was already on its way to Pearson Field.

Inside of the plane Belyakov and Baidukov were aware of the gathering crowd. Chkalov was outside with a "tall, stern-looking" man and began beating on the side of the fuselage, telling the pair to hurry because "General Marshall" was waiting for them. Baidukov was puzzled. "Is it a general or a marshal that's meeting us?" he asked Belyakov. Belyakov answered that it must be a general as he didn't think there were any marshals in the United States.

Vancouver Barracks was George Marshall's first post after he was promoted to General. He appreciated the post's history (it had been established in 1849 and was the first army post in the Northwest) and was popular in the community due to his civic efforts. Along with many other Americans he and his wife, Katherine, had followed the flight's progress on the radio. After an aide informed him that "the Russians have landed" he hustled into his Packard and ordered the driver to speed straight across the post golf course to the air field. He returned with what Katherine Marshall later described as "three polar bears."

The fliers were provided with rooms and baths. The family's breakfast of orange juice, bacon, eggs, and coffee went to their unexpected guests. Chkalov traced out their route on the family atlas. General Marshall faced the first of a long day of minor and major emergencies when the orderly announced that there were "$100 bills blowing all over the rooms and I don't want to be responsible." The fliers' supplies had included American money. They had left rolls of bills on the dressers when they took their baths with the result that several hundred dollars were blown onto the General's lawn.

Soon there were pressmen and curious civilians all over the post. The telephone was ringing with calls from Washington, D.C., Moscow, London and elsewhere. The *Columbian* reported that the "landing of the Russians here made this city a center for the greatest long distance communications barrage in its history." Ambassador Alexander Troyanovsky flew up from the Soviet Consulate in San Francisco. The Marshalls' home was packed with the press. Katherine Marshall called it a "circus." General Marshall, in the international spotlight for the first time in his career, handled the situation with aplomb. His superiors were favorably impressed.

The fliers were feted in Vancouver and Portland. Congratulatory telegrams came in from Joseph Stalin, President Franklin Roosevelt, and others. Major Paul Burrows, the field commander, received a more business-like telegram from the War Department: "Request, report to this office any data obtainable on instruments used by the Russians on their recent flight to the U.S. especially on *navigational* instruments. This considered secret." The Soviet government had already agreed to turn over any photos taken to the U.S. for processing.

The plane's three barographs, which would record whether the plane had landed between Schelkovo Aerodrome and Pearson Field, had been removed by Chkalov and a board appointed by General Marshall. The members of the board were: Major Burrows, Major Howard C. French, Captain L. B. Hickham, Harry K. Coffey, Captain Sumner C. Palmer, Brigadier-General W. E. Gilmore, retired, and G. R. Wilson. The National Aeronautic Association was authorized to act for the Federation Aeronautique International. As governor of the Oregon chapter of the N.A.A., Coffey was responsible for the barographs. He personally delivered the delicate instruments to the proper authorities. It was determined the plane had not landed. The fliers had covered 5,288 nautical miles (6,073 statute miles).

The flight had not established a new non-stop distance record and the fliers expressed regret at

Vancouver air enthusiasts had reason to be pleased in October 1929. The U.S.S.R. had commissioned a "good will" flight to the United States. Presumably part of the reason for the flight was to demonstrate Soviet aviation technology. A twin-engined ANT-4 dubbed "Land of the Soviets" made the trip to the U.S., flying over the Alaskan route. Upon reaching Seattle the plane was fitted with wheeled landing gear to replace the floats that had been necessary along the inland passage.

They were to fly to San Francisco/Oakland, then Cheyenne, Wyoming, Chicago, Dearborn, Michigan (at the invitation of Henry Ford), and finally New York City. The Vancouver Chamber of Commerce wired the fliers while they were in Seattle asking them to fly over the city. The aviators were reportedly "swamped" with such requests.

The "Land of the Soviets" did not fly over the city as requested but landed unexpectedly at Pearson Field. The Soviet plane developed an oil pressure problem in the left hand motor and landed at Pearson. Lt. Carlton Bond, commander of the field, provided the Soviets with mechanical assistance.

A number of Portland representatives came to Pearson by airplane in an attempt to convince the Soviets to fly to Swan Island. The "spokesman" for the Portland group was reported to have said to the Soviet commander, S. A. Shestakov, "Listen I sent you a wire to land at Swan Island; don't you remember?" Shestakov replied in halting English, "I - get - wire from Vancouver, oldest - city - in Washington." The navigator, B. V. Sterligov, took a different tack; he asked if Swan Island was an army field. When informed that it was not he said, "This is soladen - army - field."

The ANT-4 stayed at Pearson amidst a "throng" of onlookers and was guarded by soldiers. After finishing the repairs, the Soviets took off the following morning (October 19) and continued their flight across the United States.

not reaching California. But it was still an impressive achievement. It was among the most dangerous flights ever completed. The flight also suggested intriguing possibilities. Soviet Radio Engineer, A. Vartanian, in charge of the flight's communications in North America was asked about the flight's accomplishments. "It is a direct route they followed," he explained, "It will establish a commercial route if not a passenger route."

Vartanian's comments were rather optimistic considering the wariness with which the United States and the Soviet Union regarded each other at the time. That was another part of the flight's significance. It was one of the few examples of Soviet-American cooperation between the Russian Revolution in 1917 and World War II.

Any tension between the U.S. and the U.S.S.R. was forgotten in the excitement of the flight's conclusion. Dinners and parades were the order of the day. The fliers were fitted out with clothing from local merchants. The curious continued to come to the field, by car, foot, and bicycle.

The post bandmaster, Warrant Officer Arthur Haynes, averted a potential diplomatic embarrassment with some quick work. The formal reception for Ambassador Troyanovsky required a 19-gun salute and music from the band. The appropriate music was the *Internationale,* the Communist Party song. Not surprisingly the bandmaster did not have the sheet music for this tune readily available. After a frantic hunt, Haynes found a Russian visitor who could hum the tune for his transcription, and the Ambassador was appropriately serenaded by the post band.

The three fliers later left on a United Air Lines flight for Oakland, the first leg of a month-long tour which culminated in a visit to Washington, D.C. and a reception at the White House with President Franklin Roosevelt.

Vancouver luxuriated in the publicity brought on by the epochal flight. The *Columbian* used the opportunity to trumpet the praises of the local airport. "Vancouver airport, widely noted among birdmen for its excellent weather conditions under all circumstances, gave another spectacular demonstration of its superiority yesterday when it was singled out for the official terminus of the flight from Moscow." The aviators chose the field, interviews revealed, because it was known to them. The paper smugly noted, "It was the second Russian plane to use this airport instead of the Portland field."

A complete inspection of the ANT-25 was made by Vassily Berdnik, the man who had supervised its assembly in Moscow. He declared that the three-year-old plane was capable of flying home. But it would be shipped instead. Too big

for the railroads, it would have to go by sea, through the Panama Canal. J. L. "Dad" Bacon headed a civilian crew that dismantled the plane. He was assisted by Verne D'Autremont and Danny Grecco. Civilians were hired because there would be too much red tape in securing an army crew.

Bacon was soon the object of a practical joke. A telegram arrived addressed to "Baconovitch Aircraftski Corporationoff, Little Russia (Vancouver, Washington)." It read, "Congratulations. Glad to hear that the USSR has at last given you full recognition by sending aviators direct to Washington communist headquarters." It was signed, "Serge Beingoff Egalvetski." Bacon, who was described by the *Columbian* as "a dyed-in-the-wool American of the let-the-eagle-scream variety," wasn't sure who had sent the telegram.

The fuselage, engine, and stub wings were left intact, comprising a package 41 feet long and 26 feet wide. The wings, propeller, tail pieces, and other parts were crated. The Soviet engineer, Berdnik, could not understand why it was necessary to go through the carpenters' union to have the crates constructed. The wings, which weighed about 700 pounds apiece, were placed in 40' by 14' crates, that each weighed more than three tons. A special permit was required to truck the pieces down to Terminal 2 at the Port of Vancouver. Finally, in August, the plane was hoisted aboard a Norwegian freighter, *Beranger,* for the voyage to Le Havre, France. The record-breaking plane was exhibited at the International Air Fair in Paris, 1937. It was then transported to the U.S.S.R. by train.

Vancouver aviation supporters joined together in a "Moscow to Vancouver Committee," dedicated to erecting a marker to commemorate the historic landing at the Vancouver airport. The nucleus of the committee were "Dad" Bacon, attorney Roy Sugg (who had owned one of the first private planes in Vancouver), newspaperman Leverett Richards, and community leaders Henry Rasmussen, D. Elwood Caples, Paul Schulz,

Horace Kiggins, and Russell Elsom. The committee thought the Soviets should keep Vancouver in mind for future transpolar flights. It sent a telegram reading: "Stalin, Moscow. Vancouver, Wash. warmly invites you make terminus here for first transpolar passenger flight. Safe fogless protected field strategically located."

Three weeks after the ANT-25 landed at Pearson its sister ship flew over the pole. A group of reporters, cameramen, radio men, newsreel cameramen, "watchful army officials and just plain spectators" stood ready at Pearson Field in the event the second flight should land there. Wags at the *Columbian* editorialized that, for Portland's sake, it would be better if the Russians did not land at Vancouver a second time. "It would simply give those Oregonians nervous prostration to have it happen again."

With the advantage of their comrades' experience in the arctic this plane made it all the way to San Jacinto, California. Pilot Mikhail Gromov with crewmen Sergei Danilin and Andrei Yumashev set a new non-stop distance record: 6,306 nautical miles (7,031 statute miles).

Vancouver's pride in this international aviation achievement was commemorated in 1975 with the erection of a monument to the historic flight. Baidukov and Belyakov, both generals, attended the ceremonies. Chkalov was killed in 1938 testing a new aircraft. He is remembered here as the Russian Lindbergh. Among his countrymen he is remembered among the handful of aviation greats.[1]

Soviet engineer Vassily Berdnick. (Lev Richards photo)

Soldiers tow the ANT-25 to a more secure location. (Lev Richards photo)

CERTIFICATE OF LANDING

Record Classification: _____

Description of landing point: U. S. Army Air Corps landing field, Pearson Field, Vancouver Barracks, Washington.

Names and distances of the three cities or towns nearest to place of landing:

1. Vancouver, Washington - 1/2 mile.
   Latitude: 45° 37'   Longitude: 122° 40'
2. Portland, Oregon - 6 miles.
3. Camas, Washington - 15 miles.

Date of landing: June 20, 1937.

Time of landing: 8:22 A.M., Pacific Standard Time.

Name of Pilot: 1st Pilot V. TCHKALOV.

Name of crew or passengers (if any): Co-Pilot G. BAIDUKOV; Navigator A. BELIAKOV.

Name and type of aircraft: ANT-25   Identification No.: URSS-25

Manufacturer: Central Hydro-Aero Dynamic Institute, Moscow, USSR.

Engine: AM-34-R   H.P. 950

Were gasoline and oil tanks (and ballast, if required) properly sealed upon landing: YES

Describe method of sealing: Safety wire and lead seal.

In order to establish the correctness of the flight, the National Aeronautic Association requests the witnesses of the landing to sign this certificate and to have it certified by a notary public and returned to the pilot.

[signature]
Signature of Pilot

Full names of witnesses, title, rank, business, profession, address, etc.

HARRY L. COFFEY, Governor of Oregon, National Aeronautic Association, American Bank Building, Portland, Oregon.

Witness *[signature]* PAUL E. BURROWS, Major, Air Corps, Commanding Officer, Pearson Field, Vancouver Bks., Wa.

Witness *[signature]* HOWARD C. FRENCH, Major, Air-Res., 2960 N.E. 30th Ave., Portland, Oregon.

Subscribed and sworn to before me this ____ day of June ____ 1937

[signature]
Notary Public

CERTIFICATE
OF
REMOVAL OF SEALED BAROGRAPHS

This is to certify that on (give proper date) JUNE 21, 1937.

I removed official barograph number 15060 and also alternate barograph number 15057 from a (state make of aircraft) Type ANT-25 Central Hydro-Aero Dynamic Institute manufactured airplane, Moscow, USSR. which landed at (describe landing point) Pearson Field, Vancouver Barracks, Washington immediately following a record attempt during which time the aircraft was piloted by V. TCHKALOV

I found the instruments sealed and the official lead seals in good condition.

Following the removal of the barographs they were forwarded under my direction to the Contest Board, National Aeronautic Association, Dupont Circle, Washington, D. C.

IMMEDIATELY UPON REMOVAL OF THE BAROGRAPHS FROM THE PLANE, THE STYLUS OR PEN SHOULD BE PLACED IN THE "OFF" POSITION. TO DO THIS RELEASE THE CATCH ON THE LIFTER LOCATED ON THE BOTTOM OF THE INSTRUMENT AND MOVE THE CONTROL ARM TO THE "OFF" POSITION.

[signature]
Signature of person removing barographs

HARRY L. COFFEY,
Governor of Oregon,
National Aeronautic Association
Title or position in community.

Witness *[signature]* PAUL E. BURROWS, Major, Air Corps.

Witness *[signature]* HOWARD C. FRENCH, Major, Air-Res.

Attest *[signature]* HARRY L. COFFEY, Governor of Oregon,

Witness *[signature]* LAURENCE B. HICKAM, Capt., Air-Res.

Subscribed and sworn to before me this ____ day of June ____ 1937.

[signature]
Notary Public

Certificate of the removed barograph of the ANT-25, verified the transpolar flight was made non-stop.

Presentation of the barograph to officials.
(Lev Richards photo)

The curious inspect the ANT-4 ''Land of the Soviets'' at Pearson Field, 1929. This was the first Russian plane to land here. (Below)
(Clark County Historical Museum and Harold Kern)

The crew of the Soviet ANT-4 probably chose Pearson Field over Portland's Swan Island Airport due to the presence of the U.S. Army. Vancouverites crowed how the choice showed the superiority of ''their'' field while Portlanders fumed at the perceived snub.
(Clark County Historical Museum)

Leverett G. Richards

The sky is no limit for reporter Lev Richards who has flown so many missions for The Oregonian *in over 60 years as a reporter/pilot that admiring colleagues have dubbed him after another very American bird ''The Bald Eagle''.*

In over a thousand hours of flight for the newspaper Lev noted, ''We've been able to cover news from the air that we couldn't have covered otherwise.''

Among his best stories and flying pursuits are the eruption of Mt. St. Helens, the D.B. Cooper hijacking, the first artificial rain and snow storm (cloud seeding—1947), and the world's first transpolar flight in 1937. Fifty-five years later, when that flight's sole survivor, General Georgi Baidukov returned to Vancouver, Lev covered the story once more. The two pilots, both 85 years old, one Russian, one American, had the most interesting stories to share.

A retired Lieutenant Colonel of the U.S. Air Force Reserve (formerly Army Air Corps), Lev learned to fly at Pearson in 1938. He has made Vancouver his homeport for most of his life.

''I can't imagine life without flying,'' Richards remarks. ''It enabled me to see both ends of the Earth—I got to the North Pole in 1952 . . . and in 1956 I got down to the Antarctic and the South Pole.''

''One more thing about Lev,'' commented veteran associate and reporter of 43 years, Ann Sullivan, ''he's a complete gentleman.''

Editor's Note: We owe a special thanks to Leverett Goss Richards for his generous and honest contributions to this manuscript. Lev wrote all of the biographies (except this one) about friends and acquaintances whom he had known or interviewed. Lev has recorded more stories of Northwest aviation—famous and nefarious—than any other individual in this century. He and a very small number of others will soon be ''a century airborne''.

(Lev Richards photo)

Harry Coffey

Harry K. Coffey was born to fly. In 1911, when he was only 15 years old, he built and flew his own glider. Two years later he built and flew his own airplane near Hemit, California. By 1914 he had earned his first pilot's license — from the Aero Club of America.

He flew with the Army Air Corps in World War I. After the war he combined his love of flying with his Mutual Benefit Insurance Agency, using his aircraft to keep in touch with his far flung offices. He was one of the founders of the Oregon Aero Club and served as vice president and later president of the National Aeronautics Association, official representative in this country of the FAI — Federation Aeronautique Internationale — the world wide aviation organization which certifies all speed, altitude and distance records. He was designated to retrieve the sealed baragraphs from the ANT-25 which proved that Valeri Chkalov and his crew had flown nonstop from Moscow over the North Pole to Vancouver in 1937.

Coffey was one of the founders of the Civil Air Patrol and volunteered to help patrol the Mexican border during World War II. He made the first official landing on Portland International Airport in 1940. He was a major investor in the Flightcraft corporation, and in 1937 bought and flew the first Model 18 twin Beechcraft — which is now in the Smithsonian Institution.

Coffey died as he lived, at the controls of a single-engined Beechcraft. He encountered extreme turbulence and crashed into Mitchell Point in the Columbia Gorge near Hood River June 15, 1954.

Local balloon ascension.

CHAPTER II

LIGHTER-THAN-AIR CRAFT

"The Ascension Was A Success"

Around the turn of the century aviation was still limited to lighter-than-air craft. Balloon ascensions were an event and crowds gathered to watch them. Vancouver witnessed a few such exploits.

The first was an ascension by Professor William Lang in April of 1890. He lifted off from 13th Street and went up 500 or 600 feet. The *Vancouver Independent* declared that "the ascension was a success in every particular." A year later Professor Vilas took off from the corner of 12th and Main Streets and rose some 800 feet. From there he made a parachute jump and just missed a picket fence when he landed. About 1500 spectators witnessed the event. In 1911 the *Columbian* reported the death of Dick Miller who had made a balloon ascension on the Fourth of July in Vancouver "some years ago." Miller landed in the Columbia River and was rescued "after some difficulty."[2]

Vancouver's experience with these aerial showmen was much like that of many other communities across the country. But Vancouver would have an encounter with one of the earliest exhibitions of powered and controlled flight in the nation. This flight, which landed at Vancouver Barracks, was part of the Lewis and Clark Centennial Exposition in Portland, Oregon. The Portland Exposition authorities had been inspired by an earlier exposition.

In 1904 the city of St. Louis, Missouri, was the setting for the Louisiana Purchase Centennial Ex-position. The exposition recalled the most significant geographic expansion of the United States. It also celebrated the changes wrought in the previous century with typical American relish for economic and technological progress.

The organizers of the exposition held an aerial contest, offering generous prizes. Aviation was, after all, the vanguard of modernity and the most spectacular technological innovation since the United States had purchased "Louisiana" from France. Though it did not attract as many aviators (or "aeronauts" as they were then called) as exposition authorities had hoped, the aerial contest was a success. Thousands of Americans watched men fly in the first major exhibition of flight in the United States.

On the West Coast in Portland, Oregon, a centennial commemorating the Lewis and Clark expedition was planned for 1905. Remote from the nation's population centers and located in a region best known for its timber and generally undeveloped condition, Portland had something to prove. It wanted to show the country that Portland was a bustling, modern city. Of course aviation would be a part of the Lewis and Clark Centennial Exposition.

Exposition authorities in Portland contracted with Thomas Baldwin to fly one or more of his airships. Baldwin was at the forefront of controlled lighter-than-air flight, having been successful at St. Louis with his pilot Roy Knabenshue.

(A few years later Baldwin and Glenn Curtiss built and flew the Army's first dirigible.) Knabenshue quit his association with Baldwin after the St. Louis exposition to go on his own. In need of a pilot for the Portland event, Baldwin promoted one of his employees, eighteen year-old Lincoln Beachey, from balloons to dirigibles.

Beachey made 23 successful flights while at the Lewis and Clark Exposition. Baldwin considered this series of flights the most significant accomplishment in controlled flight to that date. On one flight Beachey was charged with the delivery of a message from the president of the Exposition to General Constant Williams, the commander of the Department of the Columbia at Vancouver Barracks. With the successful completion of this flight Beachey became the first person to cross the Columbia River by air and the first to make a powered, controlled flight in the state of Washington.

His landing at the barracks, and the reasons for landing there, reflect the origins of Pearson Airpark. The site is close to the Portland-Vancouver metropolitan area and its character (a large flat expanse) made it a logical place to land aircraft. The presence of the Army gave the site a sense of security as well as lending an official presence. (The Army itself was later pleased to be able to locate an air field on an existing Army reservation rather then having to purchase property elsewhere.)

Beachey established his reputation at the Exposition and went on to a successful career as both a lighter-than-air and heavier-than-air pilot. He was the first American to fly inverted and to loop-the-loop. Beachey was good enough to prompt Orville Wright to call him "...the most wonderful flier I ever saw — the greatest aviator of all."[3]

Two years before Beachey flew to Vancouver Barracks, the Wright brothers had made the first powered heavier-than-air flight at Kitty Hawk, North Carolina in December 1903. At the time few people knew of the flight and few of these believed what they had heard. The Wrights continued their experiments in obscurity, finally receiving the recognition they deserved in response to their flights during 1908.

> *Message carried by Beachey:*
> *Portland, Oregon   September 19, 1905*
> *General Constant Williams, Commanding Department of the Columbia, Vancouver Barracks, Washington.*
> *Dear Sir,*
> *I have the honor to convey to you by bearer, the compliments of the president of the Exposition, Mr. H. W. Goode, and to express the hope that this uniquely transmitted message will be delivered to you promptly and safely by aeronaut Lincoln Beachey, the pilot of Captain Baldwin's airship "City of Portland." In this connection permit me to say that if this message reaches you, as we now have every confidence it will, you will enjoy the distinction of being the first one to have ever received a document conveyed under similar auspices and President Goode and myself will share your honors in being the first to transmit the same.*
> *Your Very Truly,*
> *(signed)   Theodore Hardee*
> *Assistant to the President*

The Wright brothers were not alone in their attempts to master the difficulties of heavier-than-air flight. Louis Bleriot flew across the English Channel in 1909. In the fall of the same year Glenn Curtiss's pilots began flying exhibition tours. The Wrights followed with their own tour. Events such as these made the general public more aware and less skeptical of aviation. The exhibitions were also profitable. The Wright Exhibition Company annually grossed about one million dollars.[4]

Later, Beachey became a member of the Curtiss flying team. His daring exploits earned him the moniker "The California Flying Fool." But it was Beachey's imitators who were fools. Many of them were killed and the press blamed Beachey. In 1915 a wing on Beachey's new monoplane collapsed and sent him into San Francisco Bay where he drowned. Professional to the last, Beachey was found with his hand on the fuel petcock. While going down he had thought to close it to prevent a fire. Though his end was tragic, Beachey had been an integral part of the development of aviation and the heritage of Pearson Airpark.

First Airship at Vancouver, Wash.

GELATINE.

(James Raley Collection)

Lincoln Beachey flies at Vancouver Barracks, September 19, 1905. This is the first powered, controlled flight in the state of Washington. Beachey's airship ''City of Portland'' was dubbed ''Mongrel'' after its gas bag was replaced by that of the ''Gelatine.''

Lincoln Beachey at the Lewis and Clark Centennial Exposition 1905. Note hot air balloon in foreground.

16

Si Christofferson

Silas Christofferson put Vancouver on the map and made headlines around the world June 11, 1912 when he took off from the roof of Portland's Multnomah Hotel, and 12 minutes later landed at what became Pearson Field. He is said to have carried a few letters, which made it unofficially the first interstate air mail flight. He became famous for his "death dives" and other daredevil stunts. He set a world's distance record of 302 miles in one day, Feb. 10, 1914; and a new record for altitude — 14,496 feet — on June 23, 1914. He was the first to fly passengers out of Vancouver — including his bride, Edna — sitting precariously on the leading edge of the lower wing.

But he was more than a showman. Si, who lived at Vancouver, designed and built his own airplanes and his own motors and carburetors. Si never stopped experimenting. To bank and turn those early planes the pilot had to warp the wings by means of levers strapped to his shoulders. Christofferson was testing a new system of flight controls using stick and rudder at Redwood City, California when he crashed and was killed.

Christofferson's pusher biplane at barrack's polo grounds. (Pearson Air Museum)

CHAPTER III

AEROPLANES, AERONAUTS, AVIATORS AND ARMY MULES
"A Mail Carrying Exhibition"

Vancouver had had just a little experience with aviation: balloon ascensions, parachute jumps, and, of course, Beachey's unmatched aerial feat. But now the "aeroplane" was king of the skies. "Aeronauts" like Beachey were becoming "aviators." While balloons and dirigibles still attracted a crowd, the public wanted to see the heavier-than-air craft. Aerial exhibitions, staged by professional aviators, were a profitable business. The two big professional flying teams, sponsored by rivals Glenn Curtiss and the Wright Brothers, toured the country.

In March, 1910, the local area got its first heavier-than-air exhibition. Charles Hamilton, a member of the Curtiss flying team, flew at Portland. The commander of Vancouver Barracks, General Marion Maus, watched Hamilton to assess the military applications of the airplane.[5]

The following year Vancouver boosters were sure they would have their exhibition. The Portland Rose Festival hoped to have Eugene Ely, W. H. Whitman, Chester Robin, and other members of the Curtiss flying team perform during the festival. As no suitable location could be secured in Portland, festival authorities inquired into whether the barracks polo grounds might be available. Vancouverites were asked to put up $4,000 of the $14,000 guarantee that would be required to bring the aviators to the area. The Vancouver

Commercial Club agreed to raise the funds. But the arrangements with Ely and his fellows fell through, which was typical in these tenuous days of aviation. The interest in employing the polo grounds as a landing field, however, remained. It would soon be used regularly by aviators and their craft.[6]

The exhibitions certainly helped advance aviation. They developed a corps of capable pilots and introduced large portions of the public to the airplane. But the exhibitions were also something of a detriment to the development of serious uses for the airplane. When a flight had been advertised crowds wanted to see one regardless of conditions. And they quickly became bored with a stunt they had seen before. This led to pilots flying in unsafe weather (in at least one case at the prompting of the county sheriff) and to attempt foolish maneuvers. Exhibition pilots were paid handsomely, but many never lived to enjoy their earnings.

Portland had had the area's first airplane flight (1910), but the barracks was to become the center for aviation. Aviators (and would-be aviators) began to congregate at the polo grounds. The young men who gathered on the barracks flats were part of a fledgling aviation community. For the next several years aviation grew in the hands of a mixture of professional pilots, backyard tinkerers, auto mechanics, and hangers-on. Like Beachey and the Rose Festival officials, they were drawn to the big flat expanse north of the Columbia River.

Beginning in May of 1911 the polo grounds became synonymous with airplanes and the *Columbian* soon dubbed it the "aviation camp." Silas Christofferson had a monoplane built along the lines of Louis Bleriot's, sometimes referred to by the *Columbian* as an Antoinette, as well as an engine-less biplane of the Curtiss type. Louis Bleriot and his monoplane had been made famous by his flight across the English Channel in 1909.

Christofferson's backer was his employer, the F. A. Bennett Automobile Company. Like many early aviators his success in racing cars was considered evidence of his ability to pilot aircraft. He had won the Rose Festival Road Race in 1910 and, in 1911, took first place in the Pacific Coast Championship for the twenty-five foot motorboat class. Christofferson and his brother, Harry, had not had plans for the Bleriot and were forced to estimate and guess at some of the specifications.

On May 29, 1911 he climbed in the Bleriot and "maneuvered around the polo grounds at the post testing out his engines and guiding apparatus." He made a few hops of less than twenty feet with the forty horsepower craft before alighting too hard and breaking one of the rudders. In early June he "skimmed over the ground at a lively rate but did not get far off the earth" before a wiring problem grounded him. By this time he had been joined by Charles "Fred" Walsh. Christofferson continued his experiments without any conspicuous success. He had two crashes, neither very serious, which led the *Columbian* to conclude that the monoplane lacked balance and seemed easily affected by wind gusts. Christofferson was not deterred, however, and continued working with the plane.

Walsh had already flown in several places on the Pacific coast and in Canada. He owned the 118th aeroplane license issued by the Aero Club of America and was working for the Pacific Avia-

tion Company which established Vancouver as its base of operations for 1911. It maintained a plane there until 1912. The principals of the Pacific Aviation Company were H. W. Manning and his sons. Manning owned the Portland Gas Mantle Manufacturing Company. The Mannings had been trying to fly for about a year without much success but with plenty of public ridicule. They had spent $20,000 before hiring Walsh. One of the boys, Allen, had been building an airplane in a barn in Fruit Valley. It was along the lines of a Wright design and constructed of bamboo and parafined canvas. Though the young Manning, still in high school, was reputed to have "the instinct of a mechanical genius," it is not known if the plane ever flew.

Soon after his arrival, on June 15th, Walsh, "soaring far above the city and parade grounds of the barracks made a perfect flight in his new Curtiss-Farman-Walsh biplane, the first performance of the kind the city has ever known." The *Columbian* gushed that "there was not a moment during the whole flight that the big machine was not under the complete control of the aviator, and he turned, rose, or descended at will." A take-off roll of about 75 yards was necessary before "the beautiful machine seeming almost imbued with life, rose gracefully from the ground and sailed through the air like a bird." Walsh made two flights, flying over the city and then Officers' Row at between two and four hundred feet, depending on whether one credits the account of the *Columbian* or *Oregonian*. On landing after the second flight an inter-plane strut and engine mount were broken. This prevented the *Columbian's* society editor Miss Veda Potarf, from going aloft. Post commander Colonel George K. McGunengle had already been disqualified as a passenger on account of his having "the largest physique in the First Infantry."

The post's army mules seemed determined to become "air minded," at least until Walsh made the first flight. The mules pastured near the tents that housed the planes on the artillery drilling grounds. They would often poke their heads into the tents to see what was inside. One mule, who had acquired a taste for the awnings of one of the tents, had to be driven away with a monkey wrench. He later managed to get his head stuck in the tail wires of the Bleriot. "He seemed to take it as a matter of course and stood still until freed." But once Walsh took to the air, the mules stampeded. They weren't without human compatriots, however: a woman and three children on Officers' Row fled "in terror" when Walsh flew overhead.

During June, Walsh tested a device, the Ellsworth Equilibrator, designed to control the lateral guidance of the aeroplane and to preserve the equilibrium under any conditions (i.e. pitch and roll). This early "auto-pilot" was indicative of aviators' efforts to make flying safer and more practical. The Mannings' Pacific Aviation Company had contracted with inventor Dighton Ellsworth's Ellsworth Aviation Company to test the device. To facilitate the tests a light was connected to the "hand steering apparatus." The light would go out whenever the pilot operated the wheel. Five Army officers served as observers for the final tests on the 29th. Included on this committee were Colonel Rogers and Lieutenant George who were reputed to have some aviation expertise. The *Columbian* characterized them as "well posted along the lines of aerial navigation and should the War Department decide to experiment here they would be the logical ones to put at the head of the enterprise." Rogers, George, and the other officers were enthusiastic about the equilibrator after the test. Walsh was favorably impressed with the device saying that "it would work every time before I could." Despite Walsh's opinion, the device apparently was not a commercial success.

In August a "would be" aviator had his home-built bamboo plane towed by an automobile at the barracks. It was a monoplane of the Santos-Dumont-Bleriot type and weighed 120 pounds with 180 feet of wing surface. Emil Komm's plane never did fly on its own, but did serve as a prop at an "aviation wedding" at the county fair on October 7. Komm's plane had been scheduled to fly at the fair and the wedding had been scheduled to take place in a balloon. Eight couples had applied to the fair manager to be wed aloft. However, the balloon couldn't lift the wedding party and Komm's flightless plane was subsequently requisitioned for the ceremony.[7]

The following year Christofferson returned to the polo grounds from Oakland, California where he had been flying. On May 19, 1912 he became the second person to fly over Vancouver. Piloting a Curtiss type of biplane, Christofferson made two flights and rose to nearly a thousand feet. He had not sought any publicity for the flights. Consequently, few saw him fly. But curiously it was reported that many who did "thought it was a dummy machine with no one in it." Perhaps Vancouver aviation observers now imagined the Ellsworth Equilibrator had rendered pilots unnecessary.

The aviator related that the flights were necessary to acquaint him with the air in Vancouver. It was much different, and superior to, the air in Oakland. He said that "this is a much better place to fly as the atmosphere is firmer and holds the machine much steadier." The flights also quickly laid to rest any whisperings about his abortive attempts to fly his Bleriot the previous year (1911). The *Columbian* asserted that "it was this very work and experimentation that has made him a master flyer now."

A few days later he took the first women, Miss Alma Pederson and Mrs. Edna Becker, aloft over the city. Mrs. Becker declared that she would become a pilot (or "plane driver" as the *Columbian* termed it) and later did. She also eventually became Mrs. Christofferson.

Christofferson flew on a regular basis at Vancouver that summer. One of his spectators was 14 year-old T. Claude Ryan who was visiting his grandparents. Christofferson was the second man Ryan had seen fly. His first experience had been watching the continent-crossing *Vin Fizz* fly over his hometown in Kansas in 1911. Ryan went on to distinguish himself as one of the nation's leaders in aircraft manufacturing. Many members of the extended Ryan family still reside in the Vancouver area.

June saw two other planes at the grounds. Fred Meyn was experimenting with one and the other was owned by the Manning brothers who, along with their father, had employed Walsh the previous year. The Manning ship was a headless Curtiss and was "supposed to be very fast." Christofferson tested the machine for the Mannings and found it to be tail-heavy.

Emil Komm was back in the news with a new airplane. This plane, the "Komm 1," was of his own design and had detachable wings. An aviator could thus drive on the roads should he choose not to fly. The plane was 13 feet long with a tractor propeller. Three wheels, of a motorcycle type, were configured two to the front with one in the rear. Komm tested it on the ground at the Bagley Downs race track (then the Clark County Fairgrounds and now the location of Eleanor Roosevelt Elementary School), reaching speeds of 30 m.p.h. with the throttle half-open. He had this model towed by a car and it went aloft at 15 m.p.h. He even held a patent on the wing tips which were reputed to help keep the plane level.[8]

Both Meyn and Silas Christofferson's brother and chief mechanic, Harry, had flying accidents. Harry landed in a tree about a mile east of the barracks. A polo game crowd took little notice of the event and the tree was credited with averting any serious injuries to the pilot. Meyn dropped to the ground from about 30 feet and was thrown from his craft. After making a flight the full length of the field and, lacking sufficient altitude to clear a telephone wire, he had ducked under it and crashed. The entire front part of the machine was destroyed but the aviator escaped unhurt.

Silas Christofferson, operating from his base at the barracks, had a scare in which he "missed death by the barest margin," according to the *Oregonian*. Flying about dusk at a height of 1000 feet he encountered an "air hole" and dropped

"An aviational mule or at least a mule with aviational aspirations is one of the prodigies of the government herd at the barracks. He stays around, poking his head through under the hangar, and solemnly surveying the interior of the work tent, and brays his desire to soar to heights beyond. The theory is that he is a descendent of Pegasus and the blood of his ancient ancestor now stirs within him the same spirit which imbued his aerial progenitor with the desire to rise each morning, and flying far above the earth, escape its mundane care, makes him restless to be, himself, possessed with the power to soar aloft."

directly down for 100 feet. He regained control only a few hundred feet above the ground. The aviator related: "That was the closest call I have ever had and I thought surely my time had come. The air was puffy and full of holes, and my machine dropped 100 feet before I passed that apparent vacuum and struck the atmospheric cushion. I was able to right my machine then, but only with difficulty. I will not go up again when the air is so treacherous." But a week later he was making the most spectacular flight of his career, a flight off a hotel roof in downtown Portland.[9]

Christofferson said he had made about 200 flights in the biplane he used for the Multnomah Hotel flight, most of them from the barracks flats. The plane, which weighed 850 pounds, was powered by the same engine Glenn Curtiss used in setting the American endurance record in New York in 1910. He estimated that he had taken up at least 17 passengers. Members of the Twenty-First Infantry, just returned from duty in the Philippines, saw their first airplane flights when Christofferson flew at the barracks.[10]

In preparation for his flight from the Multnomah Hotel Christofferson flew the Curtiss biplane to the Waverly Golf Links along the Willamette River just south of Portland where it was dismantled. This was the first crossing of the Columbia River by an airplane. The plane was then transported to the hotel where it was hoisted to the roof and reassembled. (One of the mechanics was Danny Grecco.)

On June 11th a crowd of Rose Festival celebrants estimated at 50,000, many "perched precariously" on nearby rooftops, turned out to witness the unprecedented flight. The *Oregonian* matter-of-factly reported on the motives of some of the onlookers: "The feat of starting from the roof of a building had never been tried before, much less successfully accomplished, and many expected to be on hand to witness another of the many death tolls exacted by the new transportation science."

Those with such a morbid attraction to the undertaking were disappointed. Christofferson sped down the 170-foot ramp on the roof of the 150-foot-high building and into the air. He had been expected to rise 20 feet above the roof at the end of the runway, but was able to make only three feet of altitude. Soon, he was 900 feet above the Willamette River and on his way to Vancouver in the drizzly weather. Heading down the Willamette to St. Johns, he then flew along the south bank of the Columbia at an altitude of nearly a mile. Lost in the hazy weather, Christofferson found a moving point of reference to orient himself. The 23-year-old recounted that, "looking down I saw a little object on the water; it did not look more than a foot long, and there was black smoke coming out. That must be the ferry boat from Vancouver to Hayden Island, I thought, and then I knew where I was."

After a twelve-minute flight, he landed at what the *Columbian* called the "aviation field." On alighting Christofferson declared, "I had a fine trip and the machine never flew better. It's the only way to travel."[11]

The plane in which Christofferson made the Multnomah Hotel flight was later fitted with a main fuselage float and wing-tip floats. He flew to a beach east of the barracks where the floats were attached. The pontoon was 16 feet long and 26 inches wide. The test was a success with a flight to 2500 feet and an easy landing on the river.

Christofferson was the star of Vancouver's Fourth of July celebration. Thousands watched as he circled the barracks parade grounds. Chris-

tofferson quit his association with Bennett in mid-June and went to work for two Oregon lumbermen, Brice Wilson and Everett Cox. His base remained at Vancouver until August. Bennett remained in the aviation business by signing Walter Edwards as his pilot. Edwards also used the "aviation field" as a base.[12]

Bennett planned a full program of flying at the Waverly Golf Links for his new pilot in early August. The main event would be a "mail carrying exhibition" between the golf course and the flying field at Vancouver Barracks. A series of spiral glides, death dips, and "other feats of daring," were scheduled. The *Oregonian* assured its readers that the stunts "which he will perform will be from high altitude and will conform to similar performances which have resulted disastrously to aviators upon several occasions. He declares his ability to handle his machine in such manner as to forestall reasonable chance of accident." Edward's plane was the same one with which Christofferson had made the Multnomah Hotel flight.

Another event was the "game of aerial baseball." Edwards would drop baseballs and oranges from a height of 1,000 feet. Those below able to catch a ball would receive a prize. A "good substantial catcher's mitt" would be required of those participating, to prevent injury.

Edwards made the mail flights on August 10th and 11th. He flew from the golf course, where a post office sub-station had been established, to the barracks. Edwards quipped that "no dog will trouble me. He'd have to be a combination of a Russian stag hound and a sea gull." Over 5,000 pieces of mail were sent from Portland to Vancouver. Each piece was cancelled by a stamp which read "Portland Aviation Station No. 1." After its arrival at the barracks the letters were gathered by the postmaster and sent through the regular mails. Though not the first air mail flight in the country, these were the first interstate air mail flights. (The first official air mail flights in the United States were part of an aviation meet on Long Island, New York. Earle Ovington flew between Mineola and Garden City on September 11, 1911.)[13]

Over the next several years aviation activity was sporadic, mirroring activity nationally. Without a regular system of pilot training and lacking mass-produced airplanes, flying was an irregular activity until after World War I. Still, the barracks grounds continued to attract aviators.

In summer of 1915, it was reported that Louis T. Barin had had a biplane at the site for the last two months. He made a number of flights over the city and also flew over Portland. Barin, a Portland druggist, taught aeronautical theory at the Pensacola flight school during World War I. He was a crew member on the NC-1 flying boat, one of four that attempted a transatlantic flight in 1919. Only the NC-4 completed the trip, the first such flight. Roy Jones, long-time editor of the Clark County History Annual and an accomplished pilot himself, reported that Barin made "frequent flights" from the barracks during 1913 and 1914.

Barin's plane had been designed by John Burkhart of Albany, Oregon. Burkhart had built the first plane in Oregon in 1910. He had received training at Cornell University and built a plane in 1908. An engineering degree and a practical outlook distinguished Burkhart from many of the early aircraft builders. Danny Grecco reported that Burkhart often gave advice to local aviators. He was a technical adviser to the Army during World War I.[14]

While Barin was flying at the site Emil Komm was again trying to fly an airplane, this time with Roy Nagel. It is unknown whether their monoplane ever flew. The O. K. Jeffrey Company Airplane Factory of Portland tested one of their products at the barracks in August of 1917. At the controls was Jack Skoning of Vancouver, a recent graduate of the Pensacola Aviation School. Owner O. K. Jeffrey was later a principal in the Oregon, Washington, and Idaho Airplane Company located in Portland.[15]

(Allen Peak photo)

The equilibrator itself is quite simple consisting of two geared wheels, running in opposite directions on each side of a pair of electromagnets. These magnets are connected with a pendulum device with a pair of extended arms, which establish electric connection by dipping into mercury cups whenever the plane tilts at an angle of more than two degrees. As soon as this connection is established the electric current stimulates the electromagnet on the side toward which the plane is tipping and the magnet which is fast to a shaft on which is a drum, controlling the aeilerones, then seizes the wheel on its side and turns with the wheel. This turns the drum and tilts the aeilerones, one slanting one way and the other the opposite way so as to bring the aeroplane back to the level. If it goes too far back the machine will act the other way thus keeping it level always.

(Pearson Air Museum)

Danny Grecco

Danny Grecco had the look of eagles in his eyes from the day he was born. In 1905, when he was nine years old, he was inspired by the sight of Lincoln Beachey flying his flimsy dirigible overhead at the Lewis and Clark exposition in 1905. He was one of the men who helped launch Si Christofferson's flimsy airplane off the roof of the Multnomah Hotel June 11, 1912. To earn money for flight lessons he became a daredevil wing walker. He earned his wings in Rankin's flying school and went on to become a crack mechanic as well. He trained mechanics during World War I. He was a leader in promoting aviation in the early days.

In 1946 he earned the first helicopter mechanic's rating in the United States at the Bell factory. For years he was the oldest active mechanic in the United States. He was honored by induction into the OX-5 Hall of Fame. When Valery Chkalov and his crew of Russians landed on Pearson Field June 20, 1937, Danny Grecco was one of the first to greet them and later helped to dismantle their ANT-25 for shipment back to Russia. Some of his most cherished mementos were the tools and survival gear that the Russian crew gave him.

Spruce cut-up plant at site of Pearson Field bustled with activity during World War I.   (Clark County Historical Museum)

CHAPTER IV

VANCOUVER AND THE GREAT WAR

"A Friendly Statement from the Lumber Industry"

The United States entered World War I in April, 1917. Vancouver Barracks became a staging area for troops mustered in the Pacific Northwest. While the barracks did not become a center of military aviation for actual flying, it did play a vital role in providing for the Allied aviation effort.[16]

Spruce, a light and strong-grained wood, was used for virtually all aircraft structures. The state of Washington, with some of the largest spruce stands in the world, was the United States' main source of the vital wood. However, in July 1917, an industry-wide strike hit the Northwest logging and lumbering business. It was the culmination of labor unrest that had become increasingly violent as the companies and strikers retaliated against each other. Workers wanted an 8-hour day, an improvement in the abysmal conditions of the logging camps, and better pay.

The radical Industrial Workers of the World (I.W.W. or "wobblies") were the most visible labor organization in the strike and were blamed for setting fire to spruce forests and other acts of sabotage. Mayor George Baker of Portland referred to the the I.W.W. as the "'skunk' of today" and described its members as cowardly and as being responsible for the deaths of Americans by hampering spruce production.[17]

The lumber industry sought public support by running advertisements that were patriotic appeals. Under the headline "A Friendly Statement From the Lumber Industry," the ads criticized calls for an eight-hour day as financially ruinous and stated that the industry was "not prosperous." Striking workers were urged to return to work "before it's too late — before thousands of lives of our own countrymen are needlessly sacrificed by further delay in this most important piece of preparedness" (i.e. spruce lumber production for airplane manufacture). Patriotic appeals to the public by industries, designed to pressure recalcitrant workers, were common during and immediately after World War I.[18]

The strike was not only seriously affecting the state's economy but was hampering the nation's war effort. Air superiority, which required American spruce, was a major part of the Allied strategy. The Army organized the Spruce Production Division under the Signal Corps and sent Colonel Brice Disque to the Northwest to get the spruce out. Disque used a combination of tact, manipulation, and coercion to carry out his orders.

Disque's methods were controversial. He instituted an eight-hour day, forced the industry to improve its working conditions, and employed selective logging techniques. He paid soldiers in the Spruce Division civilian wages. This raised hackles but Disque realized it was necessary to maintain morale. He could hardly expect his men to work for less than their civilian co-workers. A company union, the Loyal Legion of Loggers and Lumbermen, was organized for civilian employees.

Members of the Legion bound themselves not to strike or boycott their employers.[19]

Lumberman H. S. Mitchell of Wauna, Oregon was recruited to oversee the construction of a cut-up plant on the flats at Vancouver Barracks. The mill was built in record time: 45 working days. Soldier labor built and operated the mill. It was the world's largest cut-up plant. The main building measured 358 by 288 feet. It contained six sections, each a complete mill in itself. Numerous railroad tracks were laid to serve the various parts of the mill. The plant covered 50 acres and operated continuously night and day. The men worked six hour shifts, with six hours on and twelve off.[20]

During the plant's operation a reported 30,000 men were employed throughout the Northwest, 4,000 of them at the Vancouver cut-up plant. A large tent cantonment was built at the barracks to house those assigned to the cut-up mill and those awaiting assignment to the forests.[21]

On February 7, 1918, the mill began production. A kiln was added to the cut-up plant in March, capable of drying between 8,500,000 and 10,000,000 feet of spruce per month. The plant produced enough material for 300 airplanes daily. Much of the lumber went overseas for Allied plane building efforts. The mill averaged 500,000 feet of lumber per three shift day, with the record being 1,415,000 feet in a working day.

During the operation of the plant it milled 76,653,429 feet of spruce, fir, and cedar lumber. The entire output of the Spruce Division was 143,008,961 feet of lumber. Of this 52,345,319 feet was used in American aircraft factories. The rest of the lumber went overseas: 41,437,047 feet to Great Britain, 34,595,701 feet to France, and 14,630,894 feet to Italy. About 30 percent of the lumber produced was not aircraft quality but was sold for other commercial purposes.

On November 13, 1918, two days after the armistice ended the war, spruce production was stopped. The remaining lumber, the mill equipment, and logging equipment were sold by sealed bid by the United States Spruce Production Corporation. The corporation, a quasi-governmental entity, was formed to perform logging and milling operations, to manufacture, buy, sell, and deal in aircraft parts. It had been incorporated in August with Colonel Disque and his aide, Major C. P. Stearns, heading a board of trustees that included prominent Portland businessmen. Some $10,000,000 worth of equipment was sold.[22]

In 1924 much of the cut-up plant was razed. The Dolan Wrecking Company of Portland was paid $1,400 for the job. The *Columbian* reported that "the Spruce Production Corporation will have the ground restored virtually as it was before construction of the war-time factory, so that the space may be utilized for the enlarged aviation field at the barracks."[23]

Spruce Mill at Vancouver.   (Clark County Historical Museum)

Remnants of the Spruce Mill can be seen in lower left of this 1926 postcard.

Spruce mill's administrative office at left was the headquarters of the 321st Observation Squadron. It still stands on the field.

(Pearson Air Museum)

Tex Rankin

John Gilbert ''Tex'' Rankin dominated Northwest aviation in the exciting 20's and 30's. He saw his first action with the Washington National Guard in 1916, chasing Pancho Villa across the Mexican border. Discharged in 1919, he returned to Spokane, where he learned to fly. He soon started his own flight school, barnstorming on weekends. In 1922 he joined a flying circus starring Charles Lindbergh as parachute jumper.

In 1923 he started a flying school at Guilds Lake in Portland, but moved his operations to Pearson Field in 1924. In the spring of 1926, unhappy with the field management, he moved to Mock's Bottom and then to Union Avenue and Columbia Street. He published a series of pocket books on flying, which inspired a lot of groundlings to try their hands at the controls.

In 1937 Tex won the title of world's champion aerobatic pilot and held it for 10 years. His protege, Dorothy Hester, set a world's record for women of 19 consecutive outside loops. Tex set a record of 19 outside loops over Portland in 1929 and in 1931 stretched his record to 131 loops. That record has never been broken.

In 1928 Tex made the first non-stop solo flight from Canada to Mexico. He entered the 1928 national air race in a plane with a huge ''13'' on the side, carrying a black cat as a mascot. He didn't win.

Rankin was killed in the summer of 1947 when his Seabee amphibian hit a power line after taking off from Klamath Falls.

Walt Bohrer, 84, who flew with Tex for 20 years, has written Tex's intimate and authoritative biography ''Black Cats and Outside Loops.''

(Pearson Air Museum/Dick Mitchell photo)

Oakley Kelly

Lt. Oakley G. Kelly, commander of the 321st Observation Squadron at Pearson Field from 1924 to 1928, is best known as the first man to succeed in flying nonstop across the continent. He took off from Roosevelt Field, Long Island in a Fokker T-2 and landed at San Diego, May 2, 1922. He was awarded the Distinguished Flying Cross for this feat.

He had a reputation as a bit of a daredevil, often flying under the Broadway bridge in downtown Portland. But he also played a major role in promoting aviation in the Northwest. In 1924 he flew Ezra Meeker, 94, from Vancouver to Dayton, Ohio over the Old Oregon Trail in four days. It took Meeker four months to make the trip by covered wagon drawn by oxen.

In August 1925 Kelly flew an *Oregon Journal* editor down to San Francisco and returned with 50,000 souvenir 50 cent pieces celebrating Fort Vancouver's Centennial. In the process he set new speed and distance records.

Kelly enlarged and improved Pearson Field until it was the finest on the Coast, next to the Army Air Service's main base at San Diego. In 1925 he tore down the fence between the Army field and the city's commercial airstrip. In 1928 Lt. Kelly was transferred to the Philippine Islands.

October 1924: Ninety-four year old Ezra Meeker crossed the continent by ox team in 1852. Mrs. Oakley Kelly wishes him luck as he prepares to cross it again, this time by air.

(Oregon Historical Society)

CHAPTER V

THE 321st OBSERVATION SQUADRON COMES TO VANCOUVER

"An Aerial Circus and Fancy Flying"

After the spruce mill was closed in November 1918, flying on the barracks aviation field was limited primarily to civilians, until 1921, though the newspaper reported hopes that an "aeronautic station" might be located at the post.

One of those flying at the field was Lieutenant William Pearson. (The field would be named for his older brother, Alexander, also an Air Service officer, in 1925.) According to the *Columbian,* the younger Pearson's claim to fame was in having taken up the eldest woman and the youngest baby. The woman was seventy and the baby seven months when they took their respective record-setting flights. William had arranged to fly passengers as a promotion for the Liberty Auto Company on an August weekend in 1919. Those who were not customers of the company would be charged ten dollars for a ten-minute flight. Unfortunately, engine trouble stopped the flights on Saturday, and a hard landing smashed the landing gear after one flight on Sunday.[24]

Soon, however, the military accounted for most of the flying activity. By 1921 the landing field was being used by the Army's forest patrol, a cooperative effort between the Air Service and the Forest Service. A hangar (or "shed" as the paper called it) was built for this purpose. The Army moved the hangar to its present location in 1925.[25]

The patrol used aircraft to spot and locate fires in forest lands. Protection of this vast natural resource on the Pacific Coast was deemed important enough for the government to become involved. In addition, it gave the Air Service a chance to demonstrate a beneficial use of the airplane, which bolstered the service's image.

Planes also used the field as a starting point for expeditions to photograph Army installations, aerial mapping of the local port (for the United States Board of Engineers for Rivers and Harbors and the United States Shipping Board), and to map air conditions. During the spring of 1922 the army used the field as a base for a campaign to attract young men to the Citizens Military Training camps. On separate occasions two pairs of pilots flew throughout the Northwest in this effort.[26]

The 321st Observation Squadron (Organized Reserves) was located at Vancouver in 1923 under the command of 1st Lieutenant James F. Powell. Powell was a balloonist who had never flown an airplane. The equipment, however, was all heavier-than-air, consisting of a DeHavilland DH-4 and two Curtiss JN-4's (*Jennies*) in "as is" condition. Still, the squadron took part in war games in Portland with five airplanes from Vancouver dropping flour filled "bombs" as part of a mock invasion on May Day of 1923. The head of the

Air Service, General Mason M. Patrick, had visited the field the previous day.[27]

During the summer of 1923 Lieutenants Albert Stevens (photographer) and John MacReady (pilot) used the field as a base for their photographic flights in the region. Part of their work at Vancouver was the mapping of the port. During the course of their work all over the country, the pair flew 10,000 miles and took 2,000 photographs of the nation's cities and natural wonders.[28]

The same summer a British ace, Captain Cyril Turner, used the field as a base while doing sky writing for Lucky Strike cigarettes. He was on a tour for the company in his SE-5 airplane. Turner was not interested in talking to the press about his "stunt flying" but had much to say about the success of commercial aviation in Europe and the inevitability of it coming to America. Military and civilian officials would soon be cooperating to make sure it came to Vancouver.[29]

December 1923 brought good news for the development of aviation in Vancouver. The War Department announced that Lieutenant Oakley Kelly had been assigned as air officer of the 96th Division of the Organized Reserves. Kelly arrived in Vancouver on the first of February, 1924. Kelly, along with Lieutenant John MacReady, held the world's flight endurance record and had made the first non-stop transcontinental flight in May 1923. The arrival of Kelly signalled the start of earnest development of the flying field. He was also instrumental in bringing commercial aviation to Vancouver.[30]

Kelly had little time to settle in before the field was in the news. The Army had commissioned an around-the-world flight for 1924 in hopes of making the flight before others could. Various countries including Britain, France, Portugal, Italy, and Argentina hoped their aviators would be the first to circle the globe. Four Douglas World Cruiser planes were built for the task. The planes were built in Santa Monica, California. The World Cruisers were sturdy biplanes powered by 12-cylinder Liberty engines. They could be outfitted with wheels or pontoons to adapt to the wide-ranging conditions they would encounter on a round-the-world flight.[31]

The fliers scheduled a stop at Vancouver on March 19th. Several other army planes would accompany them. Oakley Kelly would lead five planes from the barracks to escort the Round-the-World Fliers to Seattle. In anticipation of the occasion, Mayor N. E. Allen declared that all city offices would close that afternoon. While he declined to issue a proclamation asking all businesses to close, the mayor implied that there would be little incentive for them to stay open with the excitement expected at the field. The Vancouver Prunarians, a civic organization that reflected the importance of the county's prune industry, reported that they would be on hand, in uniform, to greet the fliers.

The *Columbian* objected to the Portland papers inference that the planes would be landing in Portland. The Vancouver paper reminded its readers that Portland did not even have an air field suitable for the army planes. "Portland some day may have a landing field capable of taking care of a fleet of this size, but so far it must come to Vancouver for such events." In ensuing years the theme of Vancouver's superior aviation facilities would recur again and again.

An extra edition of the *Columbian* on the 18th moaned "Flyers Not Coming" in a large banner headline. It had been announced that the Round-the-World Fliers would skip Vancouver. Early in the day Kelly led a fleet of five planes on a flight to Eugene to meet the World Fliers. Lieutenants Archie F. Roth, Arthur B. McKenzie, Herbert C. Miller, and Dominic A. DiFiore flew Curtiss JN-4's while Kelly piloted his DeHavilland. The reserve army fliers carried invitations from the Vancouver and Portland Chambers of Commerce asking the World Fliers to come to Vancouver. The two Chambers and Portland Mayor George Baker sent telegrams to General Mason Patrick, chief air officer of the Army, asking for a landing by the fliers.

Danny Grecco with his three-place Avro.　　(Walt Bohrer photo)

Danny Grecco did just about　(Pearson Air Museum)
everything imaginable involving airplanes. Here he
performs a plane-to-plane transfer over the Columbia
River.

(Clark County Historical Museum)　　　　　*Round-the-World Fliers over Clark County in 1924.*

The next day at noon three of the four planes touched down at the Vancouver Barracks Airdrome along with several planes accompanying them to Seattle. A telegram from General Charles Morton at the Presidio, near San Francisco, suggested that strong head winds were all that had caused a stopover at Eugene, not any desire to bypass Vancouver. Over 2,000 people turned out to see the fliers at the field. The presence of the extra planes, according to the *Columbian*, gave "the grounds their most war-like appearance since the armistice."

Though scheduled to fly to Seattle the same day, the fliers were forced to turn back to Vancouver due to bad weather. The caprice of the weather highlighted the need for many landing fields along the nation's airways. The fliers left the next morning. Later that day the fourth flier, Lieutenant Erik Nelson, circled the field, and finding his companions had left, flew for Seattle.

Later in the month Kelly headed a fleet of army planes from the field to Seattle for an "aerial circus" in connection with the departure of the World Flight. Initially, six planes were to leave from Vancouver. However, bad weather obliged them to turn back and Lieutenant Walter Case was forced to land in a field near La Center. Some of the pilots' civilian duties prevented them from leaving later and finally three planes made the trip to Seattle.[32]

In April a reservist from Spokane, Washington, Lieutenant N. B. Mamer, flying as a commercial pilot, was in Vancouver (for three days) giving rides. He also performed stunts and "fancy flying." An advertisement in the *Columbian* gave the assurance: "No stunt unless requested by passenger." He had many return customers. All the passengers, it was reported, "have expressed the keenest enthusiasm over the sensations they received."[33] Later in the month Kelly flew over Washington, Oregon, and Idaho dropping handbills advertising the Pacific Northwest Polo Tournament to be held at Vancouver Barracks. During his tour of the Northwest, Kelly had motor trouble

in Bend, Oregon, and flew to San Francisco to obtain a replacement. His return to Vancouver in five and a half hours was declared to be a record between the two cities.

The Seventh Infantry polo squad practiced daily to prepare for the defense of their title. In connection with the tournament, Army fliers performed "every stunt in the repertoire of the United States Army." One flier was reported to have looped the loop 23 times. Lieutenant Vernon Bookwalter carried passengers as a commercial pilot. He flew a Lincoln-Standard three-passenger plane.[34]

Finally, the general public was getting a taste of aviation from the air. The airplane was becoming less of a curiosity as more people had the experience of flying in one. Familiarity with the airplane made it easier for people to accept it as a practical machine.

As summer came on, Kelly began to make progress in improving the field. New JN-4 training planes were flown up from California. The local newspaper noted "most of the ships that were originally assigned to the local field have been wrecked." In July, Kelly announced his intention to raze the inactive spruce mill to provide more space for landing planes. He called the present field "too small and...dangerous."[35]

The changes didn't come soon enough for Lieutenant Ray Turnbull, however. Turnbull set down in the Columbia River when he could not obtain enough altitude to avoid the Interstate Bridge. The incident showed Kelly the need for a bigger field. "We would have buried two men if it hadn't been for the river," he said, "At the present time the men have to turn to miss the bridge before they have sufficient elevation. They haven't sufficient room to take off in." Usually, pilots had to land or take off across the prevailing winds.[36]

The reservists based at Vancouver made numerous flights around the Northwest for training and to take part in air circuses. They went to places such as Tacoma and Camp Lewis, Washington, Seaside and Eugene, Oregon, and the

Pendleton Roundup (a large rodeo) also in Oregon. The 321st Observation Squadron was even part of the homecoming celebration associated with an University of Oregon — Oregon Agricultural College football game. After a performance for the crowd, the game ball was dropped from one of the planes. The 321st was also active locally, flying on most Sundays and in Defense Day festivities, as well as conducting a mock bombing of Portland.[37]

The World Fliers returned to Vancouver in September. They had nearly completed their circuit of the globe when an oil pressure problem developed in Lieutenant Leigh Wade's *"City of Boston II."* Dubbed "America's Air Magellans" by the press, they stayed just over a half hour before flying to Seattle and the end of the flight. The stop, though informal, was the last on their epochal flight. Lieutenant Kelly was not on hand to greet them, having flown to Seattle earlier in the day with six planes from the field as to be on hand for the end of the flight.[38]

Besides the dramatic appeal, the flight was useful in developing ideas about, and gaining experience in, long-distance flying (including logistics and ground support), flying in extreme climates, and opening international airways. The World Fliers returned to Vancouver in mid-October as part of a sort of "victory tour" across the country. About 5,000 people turned out to see the air heroes.[39]

Kelly continued the long tradition of community involvement by officers of the barracks. He was able to use his position and his airplane to dramatize for the public the changes that aviation was bringing. During 1924 Kelly made a trip to the East Coast in his DH-4. He took with him Ezra Meeker, a 94 year-old man who had come to the Northwest over the Oregon Trail in 1852. Perhaps surprisingly, it was not the first time the elderly pioneer had flown. Meeker's trip by ox team had taken four months. He and Kelly covered a somewhat longer distance in four days, with 24 hours in the air.[40]

When it came time to celebrate Vancouver's centennial in 1925 city leaders had commemorative coins minted, recalling the days of the Hudson's Bay Company. Kelly sped to San Francisco in his DH-4 to retrieve 500 of the 50,000 coins. He set a new record in the process making the round trip in 10 hours and 55 minutes. The *Columbian* beamed about the aviator's "daring" and "unique flight" which would be "added . . . to his other exploits." In a more utilitarian role, Kelly dusted apple orchards in Oregon to fight scab and coddling moths.[41]

Kelly continued his work aimed at improving the field with both words and action. He talked at local clubs, schools, and the Chamber of Commerce. The purpose of these talks was to promote aviation as a practical undertaking. Like other leading aviators, Kelly realized that the public was ready to be convinced of the need for aviation. Emphasis was placed on the ability of airplanes to perform important functions. Their advantages in coastal defense and spotting forest fires were noted.

Perhaps most important was Kelly's promotion of a local commercial field. By acting quickly the community could become a center for both civilian and military aviation in the Northwest, Kelly promised. Such a development would gain business activity and prestige for the city. Air mail service which had been performed by the government in limited areas was soon to be let out for private bids. Passenger service was also a logical development for aviation.[42]

Physical improvements began in the fall of 1924. Many of the buildings of the former spruce mill were demolished or moved to enlarge the landing field. Materials for a new metal hangar were shipped to the post in October. Originally the plans called for the demolition of the "old" hangar (then situated near the middle of the present field) when the new one was built. However, it was not destroyed, but moved to its present location where it remains today. The cost of building the "new" hangar was $5,900. It would hold eight to 12 aircraft. The two hangars stood next to each other until the "new" hangar burned in 1976.

In addition, roadways were improved and the grounds graded. As the work neared completion in the spring of 1926, Kelly said the field was second only to Rockwell Field at San Diego on the Pacific Coast. The *Columbian* estimated the field (including both the army field and the Chamber field) to be 175 acres in extent. The administration building had been an office at the spruce mill. It was moved and served as a clubhouse and squadron headquarters for the 321st. Flying equipment was also improved. The base's Curtiss *Jennies* were traded for those of a newer design late in 1924. Radio sets were also requisitioned.[43]

While European nations had directly subsidized the development of their aviation industries, (France, for example, spent three million dollars a year) the United States had done so in an indirect way. Many pilots had received their training from the military. If they continued flying it was generally at government expense as reserve officers, such as those of the 321st at Vancouver.[44]

The public's perception of aviation was also directly related to military flying. During the early 1920's, in communities like Vancouver, much of the flying people saw was that of military pilots, whether it was reserves training or flying circuses put on by military fliers. Many of the commercial pilots were also reservists (like Bookwalter and Mamer). The leading pilots of the time were military men. They were winning air races and setting records (for example, Kelly's transcontinental flight and the around-the-world-flight). But as the twenties wore on, this began to change. The commercial air mail contracts let in 1925 signalled the beginning of this change.

Art Whitaker

Art Whitaker, 92 and holding, is probably the oldest living aviator in the Northwest. For years he was the acknowledged dean of aviation in the Northwest. He was also a top mechanic, aircraft distributor and inventor. He logged more than 20,000 hours of strenuous flight instruction, charter flights and check rides in the 54 years from 1921 to 1975. In 1975 he traded the cockpit for the shop. He was still rebuilding airplanes on his 90th birthday. He now lives in a retirement home in Hillsboro.

Whitaker soloed in 1921 at Vern Ayer's sod airstrip in Westmoreland in Portland. For the next 20 years he flew the classic old Jennies, Fleets, Eaglerocks — ''and the crates they came in.'' He had dozens of forced landings, but never scratched a passenger.

He was bitten by the flying bug at age 14 when he shook hands with one of the Wright brothers (he's not sure which one) at a Boston airshow in 1914. In 1921 he started barnstorming. He joined Tex Rankin's aerial circus as an aerobatic pilot and sky writer. When the Japanese bombed Pearl Harbor Whitaker joined the Air Corps and was assigned to run a flight school at Sunnyside, Washington.

After the war he set up a plant at Pearson Field to manufacture the tandem landing gear that he invented to enable bush pilots to land on gravel bars or the open tundra. In 1957 he had 30 employees on his Vancouver payroll.

(Walt Bohrer photo)

(Paul Schulz photo, Clark County Historical Museum)

Dad Bacon

J. L. "Dad" Bacon was one of the unsung heroes that helped aviation get off to a flying start in the Vancouver area. His battered old hangar was the favorite hangout for pilots and wanna be pilots. He offered encouragement and help to many an aspiring aviator. When the Chamber of Commerce leased the 70-acre sod field from the S.P.&S. Railroad in 1925 for $75 a month, they turned it over to Dad Bacon to operate and maintain single handedly. He had to pay the rent, mow the grass, sell gas, sell aircraft and repair any engine or airframe that came along. He also ran a school for aircraft mechanics. Lowell Moore was one of his first students.

When Vern Gorst won a contract to carry the airmail in 1926 he chose Pearson Field as his operations center, relying on Dad Bacon for maintenance. Dad Bacon later installed carbide lights for night landings by airmail pilots.

Edith Foltz

Should women fly combat aircraft? Edith Foltz, who got her start at Swan Island and Pearson Airpark, logged hundreds of hours flying fighters and bombers in World War II, without being shot up or shot down. The fighters she flew were unarmed — but the German fighter pilots did not know that. When attacked, her only defense was to hide in the clouds.

Edith's husband, Joseph R. Foltz, taught her to fly at Swan Island in 1929. From that day on flying was her life. She was named Queen of the air show at the dedication of the Vancouver Municipal Airport in 1930 and promptly won the dead stick landing contest.

Edith met Jacqueline Cochran and was one of the first to sign up in Cochran's A.T.A. — Air Transport Auxiliary — women pilots ferrying transports, fighters and bombers from the factories to combat areas during World War II. Foltz spent four war years in England, ferrying fighters and bombers across the channel to France and flying damaged Spitfires and bombers back to England for repairs. For her heroic service to England the Queen presented her with the King's Medal. She met Eleanor Roosevelt. Amelia Earhart, who disappeared in July, 1937, was one of her flying friends. She died suddenly of cancer in 1956 at 54 years of age. Her son, Richard Foltz, lives in Portland and a grandson, Dr. Lawrence Foltz, lives in Vancouver.

(Pearson Air Museum/Art Whitaker photo)

Pearson with the R-3 at St. Louis, 1923.

CHAPTER VI

LIEUTENANT ALEXANDER PEARSON, JR.
"One of the Finest Pilots in the Army Air Service"

In 1925 a request was made to the Army to change the name of the Vancouver Barracks Airdrome to Pearson Field, in honor of Lieutenant Alexander Pearson, Jr. who had been killed in an airplane accident the previous year. Major W. G. Kilner, writing on behalf of the Chief of the Air Service, called Pearson "one of the best known and finest pilots in the Army Air Service." Pearson had attended high school in Vancouver and worked in a grocery store there. He graduated from the University of Oregon. Kilner noted that the Pearson family home was in Portland and "it is particularly fitting that the name of this officer, who was so highly thought of throughout the service, be commemorated in this fashion." When the field was dedicated on September 16th, over 20,000 people turned out to see the air show Lieutenant Oakley Kelly had organized. Fifty-three planes from all over the West converged on the field.[45]

Pearson's flying record was exemplary. He had been one of 74 participants in the first cross-country flying race which was held in October of 1919. The route stretched from New York to San Francisco and back. Pearson won the speed contest, making the round trip in 48 hours, 14 minutes, and eight seconds of flying time. He flew a DH-4. Various speed records were set by the Lieutenant, including one for the 500 kilometer (312.5 mile) course. Pearson covered the distance in one hour, 50 minutes, and 12.7 seconds, an average speed of 169 miles an hour. In recognition of his flying skills, the Department of the Interior commissioned Pearson to make the first flight through the Grand Canyon and survey the air currents there.[46]

Fellow Lieutenant "Jimmy" Doolittle remembered Pearson from their days at McCook Field in Dayton, Ohio when both were test pilots. Pearson spent hours practicing precision flying (holding constant speed and altitude). As a result, Doolittle recalled, "he became extremely proficient and could fly a better speed course or do a smoother sawtooth climb than any of the rest of us."[47]

Early in 1921 Pearson was ordered to report to Pablo Beach, Florida, from his post at Douglas, Arizona. He was to attempt a two-stop cross-country flight, the first attempt at a transcontinental speed record. Pearson was assigned a specially equipped DH-4, with controls in the gunner's cockpit and a large fuel tank in the pilot's regular cockpit. His flight to Florida to start the anticipated record-setting hop was intentionally designed with many stops. On February 10th Pearson left Fort Bliss for San Antonio. He never arrived. Cowboys and Army pilots conducted an extensive search of the steep and treacherous country, though the Lieutenant was given little chance of having survived a forced landing.

Six days later Pearson rode into Sanderson, Texas. He had been through a sandstorm and without food for over three days before locals found him clinging to a log floating in the Rio Grande River. Upon arriving in Sanderson he went directly to the telegraph office and wired his fiancee, Margaret Shannon. His next concern was whether his plane could be retrieved from the canyon where he had landed. In April, Mexican Fiscales found the plane in an area known as "the Lowlands of the Thieves." Lieutenant Doolittle was assigned to fly the plane out. The task required gaining 1500 feet of altitude in one mile, but Doolittle was successful.[48]

As one of the top pilots in the country Pearson was involved in racing. He flew a Verville-Sperry low-wing monoplane in the 1923 Pulitzer Race at St. Louis, but had to drop out due to propeller problems.[49]

The Pulitzer Race at Wilbur Wright Field in Ohio the next year turned tragic. Pearson was flying a Curtiss racing plane that had been obtained from the Navy. He had reported flying at speeds in excess of 200 m.p.h. While practicing a diving start the plane's wings collapsed sending Pearson to his death. The cause of the crash was traced to the hollow laminated interplane strut. The strut was subject to high-speed flutter and failed. As a result of a joint Army-Navy investigation the struts on the remaining R2C (the Navy planned to use it in the Schneider Seaplane Race, but never did) were replaced with solid struts and it was recommended that race pilots wear parachutes. On April 6, 1925, the Secretary of War ordered that the landing field at Vancouver Barracks be renamed "Pearson Field."[50]

Shortly after the field was officially designated Pearson Field, Oakley Kelly got to work organizing a big dedication. When Kelly and a few of the 321st squadron's fliers winged down to Rockwell Field (near San Diego) to pick up some of their planes that were being repaired, they used the opportunity to invite their fellow pilots to participate in the dedication planned for September. On the return flight Kelly stopped at Santa Monica, Bakersfield, Fresno, Modesto, Marysville, and Redding, California, and Medford and Eugene,

Oregon. Army fields all over the west responded to the call put out from Vancouver. (Only the field at Salt Lake City wired that it could not come — they reported that they did not have any motors.)

To help offset expenses, a motion picture of aviation events was shown in Portland. In late August the squadron's fliers put on their own "flying circus" to help stimulate interest in the movies. The films included various clips of military action during World War I, shots of Billy Mitchell's bombing escapades, aerial photos of Northwest mountains, and footage from Pearson's unprecedented flight through the Grand Canyon. While normal means of promotion were employed to sell tickets, the local police did their part as well. Violators of minor traffic ordinances were made to purchase tickets rather than pay the usual fine.

Vancouver was excited about the big event. Schools were closed for the day and arrangements were made for the children to view the action from the golf course (today part of the Fort Vancouver National Historic Site — the open space between 5th Street and Evergreen Boulevard). The Columbia River Paper Mills, the Du Bois Mill, the Mackall-Paine Veneer Plant, and the Oregon Packing Company all announced that they would run with minimal crews, if at all. The Barbers' Union set a 2 p.m. closing time for their shops. Planes began to pour in from all over: San Francisco, Los Angeles, San Antonio, Seattle, and Spokane, as well as local commercial ships that gathered on the field.

About 150 army men were feted at a banquet at Memorial Hall. Newly installed Mayor O. W. Storey spoke of how fitting it was "that in this Centennial year (of the city) a great flying field should be dedicated on almost exactly the same spot that was dedicated by Dr. John McLoughlin as Fort Vancouver 100 years ago." Kelly used his turn to speak to thank the Chamber of Commerce and the military authorities for their help in organizing the air circus.

Forty-five army planes and eight commercial planes were at the field for the dedication. Three

Pearson poses with the Verville-Sperry R-3 he flew in the 1923 Pulitzer Race in St. Louis.

Alex Pearson died flying this Curtiss R-8 in preparation for the 1924 Pulitzer Race.

of the World Fliers, Captain Lowell Smith, Lieutenant Erik Nelson, and Lieutenant Leslie Arnold, were back in Vancouver. A crowd of nearly 20,000 was on hand. The throng filled the barracks and Columbia Beach (on Hayden Island).

The afternoon started with a mass formation of all the planes flying over Portland. Speeches followed, with the Pearson family seated on the podium. A one-hundred gun salute was fired. Then a flurry of aerial action started. Simultaneously there were races, stunts, mock dog fights, wing-walking, and parachute drops. Spectators could hardly keep track of all that was happening. The *Columbian* compared the action with a three-ring circus.

One parachute drop attracted more attention than the others. It appeared that one jumper's chute had failed to open. Some members of the crowd yelled to pull the cord; women reportedly fainted. Few had heard the announcement that the jumper was a dummy. The officers responsible for the hoax insisted that it was not done as a joke. They claimed it had been an effort to illustrate the importance and necessity of mastering the intricacies of parachute control. The *Oregonian*, which reported having been "deluged" with calls about the incident, seemed unimpressed with the officers' explanation.

Governor Roland Hartley sent a message that was read at the dedication that now seems prophetic. He noted that the centennial of Fort Vancouver (a replica of which now stands next to Pearson Airpark) and the beginning of western settlement had recently been celebrated. He went on to say, "When we contemplate the scenes incident to the dedication of Pearson Flying Field we can but pause in wonderment and are left but powerless to forecast what marvelous transformations will be worked in another century. Aviators taking part in today's ceremonies are pioneers in another great era of human achievement, and someday civilization will do them homage as we have so lately done those intrepid frontiersmen who blazed our western trails."[51]

The military portion of the air field, now known as Pearson Field, was designated as an intermediate landing field and reserve training center. As 1925 drew to a close, military aviation still overshadowed civilian aviation. The civilian field at the east end of the site and known as the Chamber of Commerce Field, needed steady commercial business. Air mail would be that business in Vancouver as it was for aviation generally.

TOP SECRET

The spectacular crash which killed Lt. Pearson made headlines at the time. Yet, 70 years later, the Army Air Service's official report on the crash is still secret.

John Wulle, chairman of the Pearson Air Museum, through the Freedom of Information Act finally obtained a copy of the report—only to find it had been heavily "redacted". That's a $1,000 word used by bureaucrats to spell censored. Two or three lines and scattered words had been cut out of the report. The final four-line paragraph, apparently containing the names of the investigating officers, had been "redacted" with a pair of scissors. The actual account of the accident, in all its tragic details, appears to be untouched.

The "mishap" occurred at Wilbur Wright Field at 7:15 p.m. Sept. 2, 1924, while Pearson was practicing for a Pulitzer Prize air race.

The Army had borrowed the Navy's Curtiss Racer, powered by a D-12 high compression engine for the race. Pearson was practicing a racing start, diving down to 1,000 feet, levelling off with full throttle, then pulling up after making his pass over the field. The left wing of the biplane buckled under the stress as he pulled up.

The plane began rotating rapidly, then tumbled end over end several times. The pilot was thrown out of the plane before it hit the ground. It was destroyed.

The board of inquiry noted that "Pearson was one of the best pilots in the world." He had logged 1,672 hours in all types of planes.

The investigators concluded that "this (airplane strut) must have previously failed internally and happened to give way completely at this time."

Col. John R. Claptser, commander of the Air Force's Air Safety Agency, said the report was censored "to avoid embarassing the witnesses to the accident or the investigating officers."

The "redacted" copy of the report is now in the archives of the air museum. "After 70 years it's about time that Alex Pearson belonged to history, not to military censors," Wulle declared.

AIR EVENTS OF THE DEDICATION OF PEARSON FIELD

EVENTS

Landing to a mark: Throttles to be closed at 800 feet altitude, directly over landing circle. Judged on plane coming to complete stop with wheels closest to the center of circle. Three trials each plane. Three prizes.

Curtiss J.N. speed race: Two laps around three-pylon course, finishing over field. Three prizes.

Competitive formation: Open to all. Judge on maneuver ability, elapsed time for assembly and number of planes. Two prizes.

D.H. speed race: Open only to U.S. Army regulation D.H. planes. Three laps around three-pylon course, finish over field. Three prizes.

Curtiss J.N. relay race: Each competitor to use three planes. Distance one lap around course and change planes. Two prizes.

Stunt flying: Open to all. To be judged on variety of stunts and skill shown in maneuvering. Three prizes.

Open handicap speed race: Distance three laps. Three prizes.

Aerial combat (demonstration): Observation plane attacked by two pursuits.

National Guard speed race: Limited to National Guard squadrons. Distance two laps around three-pylon course. Finish over field. Three prizes.

Commercial plane speed race: Limited to commercial planes. Distance two laps around three-pylon course. Finish over field. Three prizes.

Parachute jumping: To be judged on altitude and accuracy of landing on a mark on the field.

Wing Walking (demonstration)

Bomb dropping contest: Contestants to fly at 1000 feet altitude and drop bombs for mark on field. Two prizes.

To the reserve squadron making the best all around showing at the meet, will be awarded the Captain Eddie Rickenbacker trophy. This will be competed for annually by reserve squadrons during the summer training camps.

RESULTS

Landing on the mark: 1st: Lt. John Griffith of Kelly Field, Texas; 2nd: Sgt. Kelly of Crissy Field; 3rd: Lt. De Garmo of the forest patrol at Eugene.

Curtiss J.N. speed race: 1st: Lt. A. B. McKenzie of Pearson Field; Capt. J. R. Cunningham of Pearson Field; Lt. H. Walker of Sand Point.

D.H. speed race: 1st: Lt. C. V. Haynes of Crissy Field; 2nd: Capt. Lowell Smith; 3rd: Lt. Oakley G. Kelly of Pearson Field.

Curtiss formation flight: 1st: Sand Point Field; 2nd: Pearson Field; 3rd: Spokane Field.

D.H. formation flight: 1st: Crissy Field; 2nd: Kelly Field; 3rd: Eugene forest patrol.

Bomb dropping contest: Lts. Taylor and Haynes of Crissy Field.

Stunt Flying: Archie Roth, Adrian Van Aelst and N. B. Evans.

Parachute jumps: Pvt. Alva Button and Sgt. Henry Kruger.

(Clark County Historical Museum)

Jack Evans, J.M. Jones - Portland Postmaster, Grover Tyler and Vernon Bookwalter.

CHAPTER VII

AIR MAIL, A COMMERCIAL FIELD AND ANTIQUATED AIR CRAFT

"Encouragement to the Training of Pilots and Mechanics"

The Vancouver Chamber of Commerce recognized that a commercial flying field would be a benefit to the community. On April 27, 1925, it appointed two committees to cooperate with Lieutenant Kelly in two endeavors. First, to have Vancouver designated as an air mail center and, second, to establish a commercial field. The desire to obtain the air mail designation was sparked by the news that the government had recently called for bids for a route from Elko, Nevada to Pasco, Washington. At this time it was hoped to get a Pasco to Vancouver route and later, routes to Seattle and San Francisco.

Kelly was enthusiastic about a commercial field. The government had recently forbidden commercial fliers from landing at military fields except in emergencies. Kelly noted that there was some land owned by the Spokane, Portland and Seattle (S.P.&S.) Railroad adjacent to the barracks field that could probably be leased as a commercial field. That the establishment of such a field adjoining the barracks field would increase safety by enlarging the landing area was not lost on Kelly.

Curiously, Kelly professed to having "tried hard" to get a flying field established in Portland. It was (and is) a much larger city than Vancouver. Most of the reserve officers lived in Portland and had to pay a bridge toll to get to Vancouver. Kelly

blamed the inability to get voters to approve a bond issue as the reason that Portland had no suitable field. He estimated the cost of such a bond to be half-a-million dollars. (The Swan Island airport eventually cost $650,000 and served as an airport from 1927 to 1941.)[52]

The Chamber moved quickly to obtain a lease on 70 acres of property to the east of the military field. Talks with S.P.&S. officials found them favorable to such a lease. It was planned that the city of Vancouver or the Port of Vancouver would operate the field. However, the port found that its charter precluded it from operating an air field and the city was apparently unwilling to take on the venture. The Chamber of Commerce went ahead with the project, reaching a verbal agreement with the railroad on May 14th. Within two days Kelly had men at work tearing down a fence that separated the fields while county crews and prisoners from the barracks graded the new field and did other work.[53]

On May 22, the *Columbian* reported that the area's congressman, Albert Johnson, and the Portland Chamber of Commerce had promised their help in securing a mail contract for the new field. Lieutenant Colonel Frank P. Lahm, assistant chief of the Air Service based in San Francisco, promised his department's cooperation and expressed his appreciation for the interest in aviation shown in Vancouver. The newspaper noted that the military was interested in commercial aviation as "an aid and encouragement to the training of pilots and mechanics." In case of war there would be more qualified fliers and technicians if commercial flying prospered than if only those trained by the government were available. It could have been added that an increase in civilian aviation would increase the constituency for aviation in general, and, consequently, military aviation. If the Air Service was going to get more funds, it would have to have public support.[54]

The hope of securing a designation as an air mail center was one of the main motivations of the Vancouver Chamber of Commerce in leasing land for an air field. The site was a logical location for an air mail station. It was located about halfway between the Canadian and California borders in a natural airway created by Puget Sound and the Willamette Valley. Nearby (and larger) Portland had no air field suitable for air mail use. The local Chamber would have to convince whoever secured the mail contract from the government to land at Vancouver.

A bus line operator from Oregon landed the contract for the Seattle-Los Angeles route. Vernon C. Gorst had gotten his start in the transportation business in the Klondike gold fields in 1899. Starting out as a supply man on snowshoes, he eventually graduated to a dog sled. After moving to Oregon, he bought an automobile and went into the stage business with a friend. During the 1920's, Gorst realized that he and his fellow stage line operators would soon have competition in the sky. It was partly from these bus and automobile owners that he obtained funds to capitalize his Pacific Air Transport Company (P.A.T.).

Contract Air Mail Route No. 8 (Seattle to Los Angeles) was not Gorst's first taste of aviation. In 1915, Gorst had purchased a hydroplane from Glenn Martin. Silas Christofferson taught Gorst how to pilot the "flying birdcage," as the hydroplanes were known. However, Gorst found little interest in his aerial ferry service across Coos Bay

(Oregon) and returned the plane to Martin. Though unsuccessful in his first aviation venture, the forward-looking Gorst became successful in his second, air mail.[55] In late March 1926, Gorst arrived in Vancouver in a Ryan M-1 monoplane piloted by T. Claude Ryan, president of Ryan Aircraft Company. (It was reportedly the first monoplane to land at Pearson Field.) The pair were on a survey trip of the air mail route. The visit signalled not only the coming of air mail, but also the changes taking place in aviation. Gorst announced that the line would also carry passengers.

Passenger service was, perhaps, the most important development in commercial aviation because it made airplane flights widely available to non-pilots and thereby helped convince the general public of the usefulness of airplanes. The effect on daily life and business was (in time) profound, drastically reducing travel time and making it practical to travel longer distances.

A friendly race between Ryan in the M-1 and Lieutenant Kelly in his DH-4 was instructive. In a three-lap race before a polo game crowd, Ryan easily defeated Kelly despite the DH-4 having twice the horsepower of the M-1. Kelly explained why he thought he had lost the race. The monoplane was built by private interests in 1926 with the advantages of modern construction and engineering. "The plane I fly was built in 1917 by the government and I have to carry around a lot of useless struts and cables." The lesson, Kelly griped, was that "the government should equip the army with modern ships in place of the antiquated wagons that army fliers are forced, with few exceptions, to pilot."[56]

Kelly's comments accurately reflected a growing trend in aviation. Private interests were beginning to take the lead and the military to lag behind. As air mail, passenger service, and the training of civilian pilots by other civilian pilots began to be profitable, aviation became part of the economy. Soon the powerful dynamic of the market, rather than the congress or the chief of the Air Service, would determine the course of aviation.

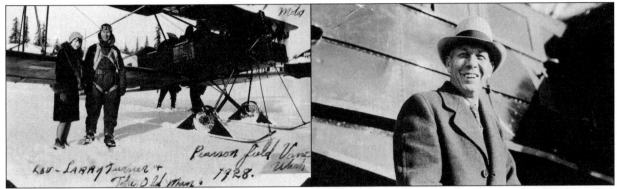

"Dad" Bacon displayed one of
his many talents by building the skis for this PT-1. Sgt.
Larry Turner poses with a lady friend, while Lt. Carlton
Bond sits in the cockpit, 1928.
(Clark County Historical Museum)

Vern Gorst, founder of Pacific Air
Transport and "Grandaddy" of United Airlines.
(Walt Bohrer photo)

Even with crack pilot Lt. Oakley Kelly at the controls this DH-4 was no match for
Ryan's sleek M-1 in a race over Vancouver.

(Courtesy Mrs. Clyde Ryan)

But the military, despite its "antiquated" equipment, continued to play an important role in aviation. Advances in metallurgy, meteorology, and physics came from the construction and operation of military aircraft. It still trained and kept skills current for most of the nation's pilots and mechanics. (Even today a significant number of commercial and private pilots and mechanics received their training in the military.) It was instrumental in opening and maintaining the country's growing system of airways.[57]

Reserves continued to train at Pearson. Not only the 321st, but also the 489th Bombardment Squadron (also a reserve squadron) based in the Seattle area, came to the field for training during the summer. Usually, two two-week camps were held. Courses were not limited to flying, but covered squadron duties, close order drill, machine gun practice, pistol practice, engine overhauling, use and care of parachutes, map reading, aerial navigation, military hygiene, air dynamics, signaling, and meteorology. Extra planes were flown in from other fields such as Rockwell at San Diego and Sand Point on Puget Sound.[58]

Reserves were trained at the field until the United States entered World War II. As the years went on, however, the activities of the reserves received less attention from the local paper and commercial activities received more.

A few days after Gorst and Ryan visited Vancouver the *Columbian* reported on another aviation business at the Chamber field. J. G. (Tex) Rankin and C. B. Harris were organizing the Rankin Flying Service, "which will operate on a scale hitherto unknown in Northwest commercial flying circles." The pair would run a 24-hour air taxi service at "auto taxi rates." Apparently, aviators were already bold enough to compete directly with established ground services. Rankin also offered scenic pleasure trips, giving Mt. Hood as an example of a destination. (Today Mt. St. Helens, a recently active volcano, rates as a more popular trip. However, Rankin accurately foresaw a use of the airplane that has continued.) The story noted that Rankin "already has the usual type of service for carrying passengers established" at the Chamber field. He also had a number of students and was to begin another class April 1st. Rankin remarked on the progress in commercial aviation in the eastern part of the United States. Fliers were "discarding their old cast-off army planes" and purchasing modern privately-built craft. He also asserted that the industry was being put "on a firm financial basis."[59]

Rankin's statements reflect the growth in confidence and financial stability of the aviation industry. That changes were taking place in the East earlier than in the West was to be expected. Development in transportation and industry have typically occurred in the more populous and established eastern section of the United States before they have in the West.

Rankin and his school went on to be nationally recognized. However, he soon moved from Vancouver in a huff. The reason he gave was the delay in receiving permission to build a hangar. However, it seems likely that the chance to be in charge of his own field was also a motive in his move to Mock's Bottom along the Willamette River in Portland.

Rankin was still a frequent visitor to the Pearson/Chamber fields in the following years. He used the field for operations when weather or high water made the Mock's Bottom site inaccessible. He and his brothers also soloed many students from Pearson Field. (Rankin returned to the field after World War II. He sold Republic *Seabee* amphibian aircraft while based in the larger of the former army hangars.)[60]

The first Northwest air mail left Pasco on April 6, 1926, bound for Elko, Nevada, and carried by Varney Airlines. Members of the 321st squadron flew to Pasco to take part in an air program commemorating the first Northwest air mail.[61]

Not wanting to lose the air mail plum, the local chamber's aviation committee agreed to build a hangar for Pacific Air Transport Company. Chamber officials felt that the establishment of an air mail center at the field would "carry with it the development of the local field." The Chamber's aviation committee also began work on regulations governing the carrying of passengers, another sign of maturity in commercial aviation business.[62]

The toll for crossing the Interstate Bridge, a complaint of reserve fliers from Portland, endangered the choice of the field for a time. But Pacific Air Transport stuck with the Vancouver field, stating that fields in Portland were not adequate for its use. In a short time the mail truck was given a free pass by the Interstate Bridge Commission, putting an end to the issue.[63]

The effect of the bridge toll issue continued, however. During discussions over the tolls it became apparent that Pacific Air Transport planned to use Chamber field only until a suitable field was built in Portland (estimated to be about two years). Some Portland officials had already realized that an airport was a necessity for any modern city.

The controversy over the bridge tolls, though short lived, provided an opportunity to convince the Port of Portland to build a field. Apparently trying to take advantage of the competition between Portland and Vancouver, Pacific Air Transport made another request to the Vancouver Chamber to build a hangar, this time for nearly twice the original estimate of $600. While continuing to offer Pacific Air Transport use of the field, the Chamber withdrew its offer to build a hangar.[64]

Despite the controversy, the first Seattle-Los Angeles air mail flights used the Vancouver field. Vern Bookwalter and others made test runs during the summer. On September 13, 1926, Bookwalter made the first air mail flight from the field in a Ryan M-1. Accompanying him to Medford (Bookwalter's portion of the route was between Vancouver and Medford) was "Pat" Patterson, who later headed United Airlines. On his return flight, Bookwalter flew a Travel Air biplane. The Travel Air, it was reported, would be used between Vancouver and Medford because it was slightly faster than the Ryan.[65]

When the "regular" air mail service was inaugurated with a ceremony two days later, the Portland-Vancouver feud again came to light. Mayor George Baker of Portland led a delegation of speakers, apparently all of them from Oregon. Lewis Shattuck, president of the Vancouver Chamber of Commerce, fumed that Vancouver was "paying $75 per month to make it possible for Portland to have the air mail and they don't even acknowledge that we exist." The Chamber may have received some compensation for their expenditures as it was reported in October that Gorst "readily agreed" to pay a monthly rental until the Swan Island field in Portland was finished.[66]

Vern Bookwalter and his boss, Vern Gorst, in front of a Pacific Air Transport Fokker Universal. (Walt Bohrer photo)

1926: *The hangar on left, constructed during Lt. Oakley Kelly's tenure, was destroyed* (Clark County Historical Museum)
by fire in 1976. The ''White'' hangar, constructed in 1921, still stands on the field.
Pacific Air Transport's hangar for its airmail planes can be seen on right.

Curtiss JN-4 ''Jennies,'' like these of the 321st Observation Squadron, were the most
(Courtesy Mrs. Clyde Ryan)   *widely used plane in America in the early 1920s.*

Curtiss B-2 "Condor" at Pearson Field for use by the 489th Bombardment Squadron.

(Pearson Air Museum)

Postcard map of Pearson Field, 1926. Note the railroad spur on left that served the Spruce Mill during World War I. The "Commercial" area on right became the Vancouver Municipal Airport.

(Clark County Historical Museum)

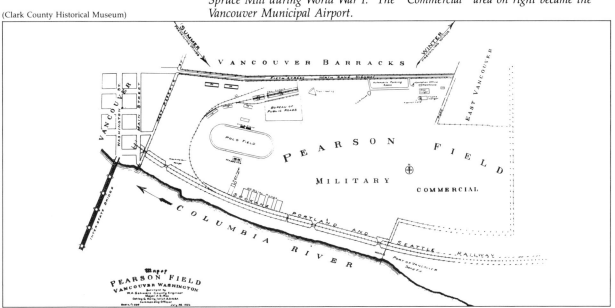

T. Claude Ryan's M-1 reposes next to a 321st Observation Squadron ''Jenny'' on Pearson Field in 1926.

(Courtesy Mrs. Clyde Ryan)

20th Pursuit Squadron and transports visit Pearson Field, 1931.

Vernon Bookwalter

Vernon ''Vern'' Bookwalter was known in early aviation circles about equally well as a savvy Alaska bush pilot and a skilled mechanic. But he was more than that.

He helped to make history when he flew the first scheduled air mail for Pacific Air Transport. He took off from Pearson Field at 5:25 a.m. Sept. 15, 1926 with 184 pounds of mail in his Ryan M-1 monoplane, landing at Medford at 8:38 a.m. He loaded up 10 pouches of mail which had been flown up from San Francisco by R. B. (Pat) Patterson and flew back to Vancouver, landing at 11:30 a.m. He was greeted by a crowd of about 6,000 spectators.

Pacific Air Transport later became United Air Lines. Pat Patterson became manager of United's Portland station.

Bookwalter soloed in 1919 after about four hours instruction in Army Jennys and Standards. He took great pride in his pilot certificate, No. 82—signed by Orville Wright himself.

Bookwalter gave aviation historian Walt Bohrer his first ride in an airplane out of the old landing strip at Mocks Bottoms in 1925. Walt's sister Ann will never forget her ride with Vern in his Travel Air ''City of Vancouver''. They crashed upon landing, but escaped injury. Harold Wagner, another pioneer pilot, had his first ride with Bookwalter, in 1927.

Vern was a big man and well padded. Tex Rankin stuck him with the nickname of ''Anti-Lift'' which Rankin defined in aeronautical terms as ''a large unnecessary object holding an airplane down.''

Bookwalter married Esther, Dad Bacon's daughter, ran an A & E shop and flew the bush out of Nome, Alaska for years. He died of a heart attack Dec. 4, 1975, at 82 years of age.

(Paul Schulz photo, Clark County Historical Museum)

The gang at the Vancouver Municipal Airport, circa 1930, standing by a
long wing Eaglerock, OX-5 engine. Front Row (L to R): Bert Justin, Charles Mears,
Freddie Sauers, Art Whitaker, Sid Monastes, Unknown, Fred Rafferty. Back Row (L to R):
Councilman Henry Rasmussen, Ed Klysner, Led Boyd, Edith Foltz, Major Gilbert Eckerson,
''Dad'' Bacon, 1st Lt. Carlton Bond.

CHAPTER VIII

THE INDIVIDUAL, THE FRONTIER AND TECHNOLOGY — *PROGRESS*

"The Great Natural Airways Converging Here Will Remain"

May of 1927 saw a signal event for aviation. Charles Lindbergh made the first solo non-stop New York to Paris flight. In 1919, Hotelman Raymond Orteig had offered a $25,000 prize to whoever was first to accomplish this feat. As aircraft technology reached a point where planes capable of such a flight could be produced, the race was on. Most of the fliers who made attempts were better known than Lindbergh and had better financial backing. Some died trying, a reminder of how extraordinary a successful flight would be.

What was, perhaps, even more extraordinary was the effect Lindbergh's success had. The 100,000 Parisians who cheered him was only a hint of this. In the United States, Lindbergh personified a combination of ideas that fascinated Americans: the individual, the frontier, and technology. A little known 25-year-old making a pioneering flight across the Atlantic, alone, with American technology was irresistibly pleasing to the American psyche. "Lucky Lindy" became America's favorite hero. The *Columbian* captured the sentiment saying that "the Lone Eagle of America, beloved of young and old as has been probably no other youth in the history of the world." Now, everyone, it seemed, wanted to fly.[67]

Locally, Pacific Air Transport reported a large increase in the volume of passenger business after Lindbergh's flight. A headline read, "Lindbergh's

Feat Reflected in Large Volume of Business Here." The service was reportedly "swamped" and reservations had to be made "two or three days ahead of time to secure a seat." Air mail also showed a "marked" increase.[68]

Lieutenant Kelly and his aide, Sergeant Larry Turner, flew to Washington, D.C. to greet Lindbergh. Meanwhile Kelly was thinking of a transoceanic hop of his own over the Pacific. The Portland Chamber of Commerce considered trying to secure the financial backing Kelly would need for such a flight. It was assumed Kelly's reputation would secure permission from the Air Corps. He would be required to take-off from Pearson Field to give the local area publicity.

A number of aviators were gathered at Oakland, California, each hoping to win the $25,000 offered as a prize. However, Lieutenants Lester Maitland and Albert Hegenberger already had the sanction of the Air Corps to make the flight from Oakland to Honolulu. Kelly was never given permission to make an attempt. They completed the first flight from the mainland to Honolulu on June 28-29, flying a Fokker C-2 dubbed *Bird of Paradise*. As Army officers, they were forbidden from accepting the prize money.[69]

In August, Vancouver was excited at the prospect of a visit by Lindbergh. The nation's hero was making a tour of the country with his *Spirit* of *St. Louis*. It was assumed that Pearson Field would be the place Lindbergh would land as J. H. Polhemus, the manager of the Port of Portland, had declared the port's new Swan Island Airport unready. The turf, he said, was not ready for planes or large crowds of people. Nor was there adequate access to the island. But by the start of September a committee coordinating the Lindbergh visit convinced the port that it would be safe to land on the new field and that a pontoon bridge could be built for the expected crowds.

The *Columbian* was understandably disappointed at this turn of events which deprived Vancouver of the opportunity to host the Lone Eagle. The paper noted that Kelly, a member of the committee which had made the decision, had sat "more or less on the sidelines" during the meeting at which the decision was reached. The story intimated that Kelly had not been loyal to Vancouver. But it was still hoped that Lindbergh might land at Pearson Field on the second day of his visit. Kelly was not encouraging, noting that Lindbergh had already been to 75 cities and would be tired.

Lindbergh passed up Vancouver and landed on Swan Island on September 14th. The expected throng descended on the island. Danny Grecco serviced the *Spirit of St. Louis* while it was there. Kelly, representing disappointed Vancouverites, asked Lindbergh to fly over the city if he would not land at Pearson. Early on the morning of the 16th, Lindy flew over the Vancouver field half-a-dozen times. Some of his passes were so low that spectators thought he would land. He dropped a message on the field extending his greetings and explaining his demanding tour schedule.

The *Columbian* report on the crowd that had turned out illustrated the effect of the air hero. It noted the "smiles of the most genuine tribute . . . on the upturned faces of hundreds." And that "they were still smiling after he had gone."[70]

Years later Lindbergh did return and land at Pearson. These quiet visits were made in order to see his sister and brother-in-law at Ridgefield (a small community north of Vancouver). Long-time Pearson operator Ken Poe has Lindbergh's signature in his log book.[71]

Several aviation firms were located on the field (i.e. the commercial field) at this time. L. C. "Hap" Roundtree had a hangar and 11 students in January. Roundtree, a flier since 1919, declared the Vancouver field as superior to the Swan Island field. Bell Line Air Service Company located its headquarters on the field. The firm operated a school and provided sightseeing flights. By November, Bell had 30 students. The newspaper noted that four of them were women. The company's passenger service was thriving. It was reported that "large crowds" were at the field each Sunday and that on one day, 250 people were "initiated into air craft by flights in the air."[72]

The stepped up activity by private interests at the field was increasing the public's ability to experience flight. The local paper recognized the maturation taking place in the aviation industry.

An article entitled "Vancouver Flying Fields Being Developed into Real Airports," noted the changes that had taken place over the previous two years. It went on to observe that "during most of the year there is a considerable sky traffic converging at the fields, not only of those planes and pilots on regular or scheduled trips but also of unannounced and often unknown planes. Commercial planes make regular trips to and from the field, of course, and the number of these trips is increasing steadily. Army fliers also are busy most of the time when weather is suitable."[73]

With a steady income from air mail, Pacific Air Transport began regular passenger service in 1927. A Travel Air cabin plane with a capacity for four passengers and two six-passenger Fokker cabin planes were purchased for the service during April. The increasing number of passengers that were being carried in the mail planes had motivated the purchase. A hangar was built in October to house one of the Fokkers.[74]

Celebrated ''Dad'' Bacon did a little of everything in his shop. Here he builds a wing for some fortunate soul.

''Dad'' Bacon works on an engine rebuild.

A Bush Flying Service Alexander (Pearson Air Museum)
Eaglerock is prepared for an instructional flight, 1926.

The Bush Flying Service was one of a (Pearson Air Museum)
number of firms that operated from the commercial portion of Pearson Field.

Scotty McFarland and Danny Grecco.

Vancouver's Municipal Airport (now part of Pearson Airpark) circa 1930. Plane is a Waco Kinner owned by ''Dad'' Bacon.

(Clark County Historical Museum)

Alexander Eaglerock on the commercial field. The ''Paramount'' hangar in background was used by Art Whitaker's Paramount Flying Service.

(Pearson Air Museum)

This Mohawk Pinto *had a reputation as a ''spinner.''*

(Horace Sharon photo)

63

Some of the planes passing through Pearson reflected the ongoing changes in aircraft technology. Four Boeing 40-B mail planes were described by the *Columbian* as "giant biplanes." The new planes, carrying officials of Boeing Air Transport, were to be used on the transcontinental and coastal mail runs. They sported both a "Boeing System" logo and "Pacific Air Transport" logo on their sides, a visual reminder of the coming of United Airlines.[75]

During August, a Fokker trimotor touched down. On board were Congressman Frank James of Michigan and Major Henry Clagett, air chief of the Ninth Corps area. Trimotors built by firms such as Fokker, Ford, and Boeing were the first "real" airliners. Though primitive by later standards, the *Columbian* described them as "luxurious." It was reported that, despite the long air journey, the passengers stepped out as though they were "alighting from a Pullman palace sleeper."[76]

Military planes showed a change, too. The Curtiss *Jennies,* used by the Army since 1917, were retired. Consolidated PT-1's replaced the *Jennies* at Pearson Field. The planes were also the first with the "PT" (for primary trainer) designation.

In September 1927, Marine and Navy planes visited the field. The planes flew over the Vancouver area making a "murderous sound." The paper noted that the flights by these planes allowed residents "to get acquainted with the speedy ships that the taxpayers' money is building for their Uncle Sam's defense."[77]

On September 26, the field had a well-known visitor who was destined for greatness. Lieutenant "Jimmy" Doolittle flew into Pearson and was called "the Army's wizard of the air" by the *Columbian.* In a fly-by, Doolittle, "contemptuous of danger and of the earth hurtled upside down along the field only a little way above the ground in his bullet-like little fighting craft."[78]

The National Air Derby in Spokane provided an opportunity for some aerial promotion of Vancouver. Vern Bookwalter agreed to let the Chamber of Commerce paint "City of Vancouver,

Washington" on the side of his OX-5 powered Travel Air. He entered the Class B race from San Francisco to Spokane. The class was limited to craft with engines displacing less than 300 cubic inches.

A veteran mail pilot, Bookwalter had flown the route between Seattle and San Francisco many times. This familiarity with the route was thought to give Bookwalter an advantage over many of his competitors. The *Columbian's* enthusiastic contention that Bookwalter "could almost fly it [the race] in his sleep," would prove ironic. After leaving a fuel stop at Medford in the lead, Bookwalter disappeared.

He reappeared the next morning in Eugene, tired and with a cut cheek. He reported that he had been flying low due to fog when his engine quit. "I had to land quick," he related. He had been attempting to short-cut over the mountains and became trapped between two layers of fog. Bookwalter blamed the crash on his own "pig headedness" and preignition of a defective spark plug. His long tramp out of the woods took him through brambles and brush (thus the cut cheek). He was also stalked by a curious, though apparently unhungry, cougar. Bookwalter, however, maintained that the cougars (plural) "meant him some harm."

Bookwalter returned to southern Oregon and his wrecked plane. The wheels and "a few other trinkets" were recovered. The plane was considered a total loss. This time Bookwalter reported no cougars, but did suffer plenty of stings from yellow jackets.[79]

At least his next reported encounter with fog turned out better. Flying a Pacific Air Transport plane he was forced down near Longview, Washington. Two boys, about 14, rushed up to the plane, full of curiosity. After showing a few features of the plane to the boys, Bookwalter asked them to "guard" it. He was worried about cows or horses damaging it. Returning at 2 a.m. with the sheriff, he found his two "guards" fast asleep in the cockpit. Pacific Air Transport air mail regulations forbade him from giving the boys a ride in the plane, so officials in Vancouver gave each of the boys five dollars.[80]

Things were changing in the aviation business. N. B. Evans, divisional superintendent of Pacific Air Transport with headquarters at Vancouver, commented on how aviation was progressing in early 1928, in the wake of Lindbergh's inspiring flight. Evans declared that the public was "air-minded" and stated the company's intention to obtain "new and more effective equipment." Evans noted that the change in public perceptions had been rapid. "Within the past year, the people of the Pacific coast have seen the air transport companies emerge from comparative obscurity to become an important factor in transportation systems of the West."[81]

Only two weeks later, Evans announced a change that would have long-term effects on the industry. Pacific Air Transport was taken over by the Boeing Airplane Company. P. G. Johnson of Boeing was named president of Pacific Air Transport, while Vern Gorst, founder of the company, was designated vice-president. R. C. Bradshaw of Portland was selected as secretary and two other leading Portlanders, Julius Meier and J. C. Ainsworth, were appointed as members of the new board of directors. This change in ownership would later lead to Pacific Air Transport becoming part of United Airlines.[82]

There were changes at the local level as well, though they probably reflected growth in the industry rather than changes at Pacific Air Transport. Vernon Bookwalter, who had flown the first air mail out of Vancouver, left for Chehalis, Washington to fly for the St. Johns Motor Company's flying service. Lon Brannan, Pacific Air Transport mechanic, went to the Seattle Flying Service as chief pilot. Brannan did have kind words for the field when he left. "I hope the Seattle field is half as good as the Vancouver airport. I'm not familiar with the field up there, but this one is hard to beat."[83]

In addition to changes on the commercial end of the field, there was a change in the military

On a Saturday afternoon in June 1926, the fliers of the 321st Squadron were taking their training flights as usual. Lt. Henry Goode received permission to fly Lt. Oakley Kelly's De Havilland DH-4. He took a passenger, Lt. Julius Syfford, a reserve officer assigned to quartermaster duties at the post.

After take-off flames were seen to come from the right exhaust. With only about 200 feet of altitude, Goode tried to turn back for a landing. The plane apparently slipped out of the bank, crashed, and burst into flames. Goode was crushed by the plane and killed instantly. Syfford had been thrown from the plane and was rushed to the post hospital where he succumbed to burns. The first fatal crash at Pearson was blamed on a "thrown" connecting rod.

The following spring witnessed the first civilian calamity. On April 24, 1927, Danny Grecco was flying his 90-horsepower Avro biplane. Two Portland telephone operators wanted to go flying with him, but neither would go up alone. Grecco finally agreed to take the pair aloft.

The plane only climbed 200 feet on take-off before plunging into the nearby railroad embankment. Both women were killed instantly. Grecco, in critical condition, was rushed to St. Joseph's Hospital. After a lengthy convalescence, he recovered. Typical of the morbidity surrounding accidents, the police had difficulty in preventing souvenir hunters from carrying off the wreckage.

On April 4, 1929 Lt. Ralph A. Floyd crashed on a landing approach and was killed instantly. His passenger, Portland police lieutenant Asa Clements, died within hours of the accident. Floyd, a longtime flier and reserve officer of the 321st Squadron, was approaching the field from the west when he apparently made a turn at too low a flying speed. The plane "side-slipped" and crashed. Field commander Lt. Carlton Bond called the crash "just one of those things that happen," after an investigation.

In July of the same year a new recruit at the barracks drowned in the Columbia River after a parachute jump. Conrad Blatter had become involved in a conversation about a parachute with some other enlisted men and volunteered to make a jump from a civilian plane. Blatter made what seemed to be a perfect descent from a plane piloted by Charlie Mears. But the wind blew him over the river and he became entangled with the chute after landing in the water. Efforts to revive him failed. Army authorities maintained that the authorities at the municipal field should not have allowed the flight. But an investigation by U.S. Dept. of Commerce inspector, W. L. Shields, exonerated Mears and the field authorities.

Two weeks later on August 4, an inexperienced glider pilot was involved in a serious crash at the field. J. W. Reubens was piloting a glider belonging to the Portland Glider Club. As he was towed by automobile at the municipal airport he apparently panicked when the tow cable did not release. The craft took a sharp dive from an altitude of about 30 feet. Reuben's skull was fractured.

command. Kelly was ordered to the Philippines. Before Kelly left Vancouver, the War Department awarded him the Distinguished Flying Cross for his part in the non-stop transcontinental flight of 1923. The *Columbian* noted that Kelly and Macready (who was also awarded the Distinguished Flying Cross) were only the fourth and fifth recipients of the award. (Charles Lindbergh had received the first Distinguished Flying Cross for his solo transatlantic flight. The second and third went to Lieutenants Lester Maitland and Albert Hegenberger for their flight from Oakland to Hawaii in their airplane *Bird of Paradise*.)[84]

Captain Aubrey I. Eagle was to replace Kelly at Vancouver. Eagle had been in the Air Corps since 1917. He was like Kelly in that he promoted the expansion of both military and commercial aviation at Vancouver.[85]

Before leaving, Kelly reflected on the changes in aviation in the four years he had been at Vancouver. "The first winter I was here, I made four round trips to San Francisco and back to Pearson field and it was considered a fair record. Now the mail makes a round trip daily." But Kelly warned that the advances already made could be lost if the community was not vigilant. He cautioned against letting either the Army or commercial fields deteriorate. "Some of you remember the narrow runway of a few years ago when an old mill and fences blocked the way down on the field." He urged his listeners to "keep it free of obstructions and by no means allow the commercial field to go by." Kelly understood the important relationship between the military and commercial portions of the field.[86]

Activity at the field seemed to indicate that Kelly's words were being heeded. The Bush Flying Service ordered six new planes in March — five Wacos and a Travel Air. Owner W. C. Bush also had a new hangar built for the company's use. It was the fourth hangar on the commercial portion of the field. In June, the *Columbian* reported on Pacific Air Transport's "new air transport service." The company had purchased four new Boeing cabin planes costing $25,000 each. The ships could carry four passengers (in a heated cabin) and 1000 pounds of cargo at a cruising speed of 110 m.p.h. Two of the new planes operated between Vancouver and Oakland and two between Oakland and Los Angeles. The Vancouver - Seattle leg was handled by a six-passenger Fokker. Flights were available every day except Monday.[87]

The Ford Reliability Tour made a stop at Vancouver in July, 1928. The all-metal Ford Stout tri-motor, the "latest thing" in passenger aircraft, was the biggest attraction of the tour. David Levy, the first pilot into Vancouver from Tacoma (after a 58 minute flight) thought the field was "as good a natural landing field as anyone could wish to have." Martin Jensen, visiting with his *Aloha* which had taken second place in the Dole Hawaiian Flight the previous year, also thought it a natural landing field. Jensen, however, suggested improvements, including a cross runway. (A cross runway was later developed. It was shut down, however, to allow construction of the replica of the Hudson's Bay Company Fort Vancouver.)[88]

The opening of Portland's Swan Island Airport the previous year (1927) cast some uncertainty over Pacific Air Transport's future at Vancouver. The consensus among those close to aviation was that the Vancouver field lacked facilities such as shop equipment, lights, rest rooms for the Sunday crowds of spectators, and even water to fill radiators. Chamber of Commerce officials wondered how they could care for "this costly but wonderfully promising infant, Aviation." The *Columbian* compared the rate at which aviation was growing to "the astonishing speed of a mushroom." It also noted that Portland had invested $650,000 in the airport at Swan Island. However, the Portland field charged higher use rates and required metal hangars which were more expensive than the wooden hangars at Vancouver. These higher costs gave Pacific Air Transport and other flying services a reason to stay in Vancouver at least for the time being.[89] As late as July, Pacific

Air Transport vice-president and general manager H. A. Humphries said a move to Portland was not anticipated. Still, continued use of the Vancouver field depended "on future developments entirely," including the possible inauguration of night flying. It was clear that Pacific Air Transport expected improvements if it was to stay at Vancouver.[90]

In autumn, Pacific Air Transport decided to move to Swan Island. The *Columbian* attributed the move to the "pressure of Portland interests." Despite sounding like "sour grapes" the paper's analysis may not have been entirely inaccurate. The company's new Board of Directors included some powerful Portland businessmen. (Julius Meier was among the largest stockholders with $30,000 worth of stock. Other prominent Portlanders owned lesser amounts.) Yet it was still the lack of facilities and someone to manage the airport that were the Vancouver field's biggest handicaps.[91]

In late May (1928) the *Columbian* produced a special section called "Progress." The stories in this section highlighted business and other activities in the community and forwarded the image of Vancouver as a vigorous, modern city. One story was about the commercial and Army fields. The combined fields, the story said, were "recognized as the finest airport in the Northwest and the second largest on the Pacific coast." The airport made Vancouver "one of the important air centers in this region." The convenience of the fields was noted. "They are less than three-quarters of a mile from Vancouver's heart, and no matter how the city grows their strategic location will only be increased in attractiveness."

Besides its proximity to downtown, the airport was also located at the conjunction of two natural airways. That from Puget Sound to the Portland - Vancouver area and the Columbia River Gorge route cutting through the Cascade Mountains. Improvements to the fields were cataloged. Four frame hangars were located on the commercial field. One each being owned by the Chamber of Commerce, Pacific Air Transport, Bell Flying Service, and Bush Flying Service. The Army field had two hangars, one frame hangar (still standing and in use) which housed "shop equipment mostly" and "a big black metal hangar" (which burned down in 1976).

The "Progress" story also offered a brief history of the airfield. One column was headlined "Beachey Started It." "Twenty-two years ago was when progress first pointed its finger at the future airport, but probably no one recognized the hint then. That was when Lincoln Beachey, daring youth, electrified the community with his flight . . . After Beachey, it was still a cow-pasture and a good one for years. But naturally when the first airplane hopped cautiously from one spot to another they used it, for the same reason that a duck would use a pond of water. It was a natural field. Then came the World War, and America's need for many, many airplanes. The Spruce Production corporation needed a site. Where better than the level expanse of the cow-pasture? And so its surface was crossed by rails and cluttered with piles of lumber and usurped by buildings. But there was so much room that airplanes could still use the field, and a few of them did."

In keeping with the theme of progress the story went on on an optimistic note. "Looking ahead, the men who know see a bright future for this magnificent natural airport if it is managed with alert and aggressive policies. The great natural airways converging here will remain. The need for travel over them will grow, probably beyond even the present visualization of careful observers." The paper echoed the sentiments of Kelly, Eagle, and local officials who felt that an airport was essential to the community.[92]

The rapid changes taking place in the aviation business and competition from the new Swan Island airport in Portland made it clear that improvements would have to be made at the Vancouver field. The local field lacked lights, a good entrance road, adequate shop facilities, and a water source to fill radiators. In addition, there was really no one in charge. The difficulty in effecting such improvements was a lack of funds.

Three alternative plans were talked about. These involved having someone other than the Chamber run the field. The Port of Vancouver, private interests, and the city were considered. The Port of Vancouver would apparently need special legislation to allow it to operate an airport. It was considered likely that private concerns would be willing to take over the field but it was feared they would not develop the field "progressively and permanently."

The Chamber of Commerce, which was then operating the field, felt the city should take it over. The following month Mayor John P. Kiggins announced that he would look into the possibility of a long-term lease with an option to purchase from the S.P.&S. railroad. Councilmen Gene Teter and George Lamka expressed their support for the mayor's plan. The mayor expressed the opinion that the city needed an airport. "Cities everywhere are going into the air business. We have more natural advantages than most. A city to keep pace with the times should encourage air transportation." In November the city obtained a one-year lease.[93]

The following year (1929) the airport became involved in controversy. Councilman Lamka purchased four and one-third acres of land north of the city field and east of Pearson field. Hangars were to be built on the site immediately and the tract turned over to the city "at cost at the first opportune time." Lamka was a member of both the city council and Chamber of Commerce aviation committees.[94]

A proposal for an emergency appropriation of $750 to hire an airport manager for six months at $100 a month with $150 for incidental expenses sparked debate in the council. Councilman Vyrett L. Chamberlain made heated objections, accusing Lamka of having "a personal rather than altruistic interest in the development" of the airport. Chamberlain also complained that there was no definite plan and that Lamka "was the aviation

committee and did as he pleased, building for himself instead of for the city." Lamka pointed out that the other two aviation committee members (Councilmen Edward M. Blurock and Ralph L. Morgan) could outvote him at any time. Finally, Chamberlain voted for the proposal provided that a new aviation committee be appointed and that the city be allowed to check Lamka's plans in developing his parcel.

However, the controversy heated up again in August. John Kirch, the new airport manager resigned. He felt that the situation at the field was unstable and a "mess." And he had not been paid. An emergency appropriation for $750 had not been approved. Uncertainty over the future of the railroad land (no agreement to purchase it had been reached with S.P.&S.), a lack of an agreement with Lamka, and concerns over liability made the council hesitant to commit funds to the airport. Chamberlain intimated that Lamka should take over the field as a sub-lessee.[95]

Two weeks later the council did turn the field over to Lamka. The written agreement (which had been proposed by Lamka) proposed that Lamka take over the city's lease of 72 acres with the S.P.&S. Railroad, manage the airport, and hold the city free from damages. The city would turn over the hangars on the field and the rent accruing from them to Lamka and make the lease payments for September and October (which amounted to $150). Lamka stated (but did not put into the written proposal) that whenever the city wished to resume operation of the field he would be willing to reach an agreement with it. The council accepted Lamka's proposal with Henry Rasmussen voting against it.

Mayor John Kiggins recounted a "lengthy" meeting with S.P.&S. officials concerning the possibility of purchasing the 72-acre tract. (The railroad had earlier indicated that it would not consider the long-term lease the city was interested in.) The results of the meeting were inconclusive. Railroad officials claimed the land was valuable for industrial development and worth $600 an acre.

Kiggins, with the county assessor in tow, noted it was assessed at $80 an acre. A price of $350 an acre was suggested by the mayor who told the council it was possible a lower price could be secured. The S.P.&S. representatives took the $350 price back to their superiors for further consideration. The city's lease with the railroad would expire at the end of the year. Lamka said the city could renew its lease and he would be ready to "cooperate" or the city could let Lamka "make arrangements himself."[96]

An air derby, including a race, stunting contest, and parachute jumps, was part of the year's Independence Day celebration. The 321st Observation Squadron demonstrated formation flying. Major Gilbert Eckerson of the 321st was billed as a "spectacular feature" of the derby and performed stunts in a Waco *Special*. As part of a larger three-day celebration, there was a polo tournament and a "Goddess of Liberty" was chosen by popular vote. Margaret Stewart, sponsored by the personnel at the barracks, won the contest. She was given the key to the city by Mayor Kiggins. She was flown to the air derby by Sidney Monastes in the Columbia Empire Flying Service's Alexander *Eaglerock*, the derby's official plane.

The race was sanctioned by the National Aeronautical Association. Dick Rankin won the 30-mile race in a Waco 10. Sidney Monastes took second in an Alexander *Eaglerock*. The stunting contest ended with Al Adams, first, Dick Rankin, second, and Al Greenwood, third. Several entries had been disqualified as a result of being "souped up."[97]

The Louis Proctor Air Jubilee, slated for August, was a major reason the city chose not to close the municipal field. Proctor, a 19-year-old Vancouverite, had won a national model competition in Detroit. Part of his prize was a trip to Europe. Proctor was associated with Neville "Jim" Walker, who invented the "U-control" control line for flying model airplanes. Walker founded American Junior Aircraft Company which produced a variety of flying balsa wood models.

Some of these were even used as targets for gunnery practice during World War II. Walker went to Detroit with Proctor to explain the details of Proctor's model. This apparently was not necessary as the judges awarded Proctor the prize without having examined these details.

Proctor spent all of his spare time at Pearson Field from 1923 to 1930. He was working in "Dad" Bacon's shop when he won the contest. His work at the shop involved such things as repainting logos on tail surfaces and doping wings. Proctor said he would do any work that would earn him some flying time.

While Proctor was still in Europe, plans for the Air Jubilee got underway. A newspaper story promised that "something will be doing virtually every instant of the afternoon of August 18...at the municipal airport." The Seventh Infantry band was to play "if anytime during the afternoon the air is not filled with the hum of airplane motors."

Two races were scheduled. One started in Yakima, Washington and was open to planes powered with Curtiss OX-5 engines. It offered a first place prize of $120 and a Lindbergh wristwatch. Four other prizes of $75, $50, $40, and $25 were offered. The race was conducted under National Aeronautical Association rules.

The other race was a relay involving three teams of two planes each. A five-mile circuit was laid out and a team member would ride in the first plane as it flew the circuit and then change to the second plane which would then fly a circuit. First prize for this race was $60 and engraved pencils for both the pilots and the passenger. Second place was $40. A stunting competition offered a first prize of $50 and a fire extinguisher, $30 for second, and $20 for third. The competition had a prescribed series of maneuvers: "Ships will take off in the order drawn and fly in large circles for altitude, each coming over the airport in his regular order, start spinning east, make at least three turns and come out facing east and at a 2,000 foot elevation. Three loops, three immelmanns (An immelmann turn is a maneuver in which an airplane is first made to complete half of a loop and is then rolled half of a complete turn. It is also known as a reverse turn.) and three barrel rolls in any combination could be made providing that each stunt was complete. The ships were not to get below 1,500 feet in elevation at any time.

A balloon bursting contest had a first prize of $40 and an engraved pencil, $25 for second, and $15 for third. Johnnie West, one of the original 13 Black Cats of Hollywood (a nationally known team of stunt fliers and wing walkers), was to perform a series of "aerial stunts." The day's events, which were to end with a parachute drop, predictably included a model contest.

The *Columbian* noted that the Jubilee would bring publicity to Vancouver. In this way it was like many aviation events across the country. Civic boosters saw the excitement and modernity of aviation as a way of promoting their community. A souvenir cachet or stamp was planned but it is unknown if it was ever produced. Five thousand souvenir programs were said to have been printed.

The Jubilee attracted a crowd estimated at 15,000 persons. A number of the planes in the race from Yakima had to land along the route due to poor weather. Les Meadows, piloting a Travel Air, won the race with a time of two hours, three minutes. Dick Rankin was second in a Waco, followed by Frank Kammer in an Alexander *Eaglerock*, and Clarence Murray in an American *Eagle*.

Shields Clark and E. E. Parmeter won the relay race with the Rankin-Kammer team second. Kammer won the balloon bursting contest with a time of 23 seconds. Parmeter was second, taking one minute and 25 seconds. No one else was able to burst their balloon. Rankin "easily" won the stunting contest with Meadows second and Parmeter third. All prize money was paid in full after the meet. According to Chamber officials the event was a "decided financial success." All revenue above expenses was placed in an airport fund.

Louis Proctor got the most enthusiastic reception from the crowd, receiving even more applause than the event's headliner, Johnnie West. Proctor, back from his trip on which he met French and English royalty and leading aeronautical officials, was more impressed with his homecoming than the aristocracy of Europe. His remarks to the crowd consisted of two thoughts: "I'm home, I'm glad."[98]

In September Varney Airlines announced that it would use the Vancouver airport for some of its mail flights on its newly awarded "eastern" route that went to Pasco, Washington. Planes were to use Vancouver for the morning stop and Swan Island for the evening stop.

A Stearman *Speed Mail* plane with a capacity of 1,600 pounds and a 525 horsepower Wright engine (145 m.p.h.) was used on the route. However, the inaugural flight on September 15 did not take place because the mail plane was fogged in at Swan Island. The *Columbian* could not resist the opportunity to trumpet the advantages of Vancouver's airport over Portland's. It noted that while Swan Island was fogged in, "the Vancouver port was bathed in sunshine; true it was rather dim sunshine, but the field itself was clear and experts said that any ship could have taken off from this field at any time during the day yesterday without any danger at all." It is not clear if Varney used the field as a regular stop, but it did use it when Swan Island was unusable due to weather and for other reasons. The *Columbian* felt this use demonstrated the "superiority" of the Vancouver field over Swan Island.[99]

The airport question reappeared in early October. The *Columbian* remarked playfully on "Vancouver's erstwhile municipal airport." Councilman Lamka had graded his acreage north of the S.P.&S. land and moved one of the hangars onto it. The railroad had, however, indicated that it would not lease to a private individual. Further complicating matters, the city attorney suggested that Lamka, as a public official and member of the council, probably could not legally sub-lease from the city. As a result, the city had probably been liable for the airport over the previous month-and-a-half regardless of any agreement with Lamka.

The newspaper article concluded by comparing the problems surrounding the airport to "the cat that would not drown." [100]

At the October 21 meeting, the council dealt with the "airport problem" again, but without success. Lamka wanted $2,000 to step down from the airport. He accounted for $800 of expenses and insisted that he could explain the other $1,200 to the council "whenever they wished." A bond issue to finance the airport was suggested, but the mayor was pessimistic about its chances of passage. Austin McCoy, Chamber of Commerce president, was in the audience and Mayor Kiggins suggested a take over of the field in an exchange which brought laughter from the audience.

"I wonder if the Chamber wouldn't like to take over the field," said the mayor, "Don't you think it would be a good idea Austin? It would save us all this trouble."

"I believe the Chamber would be glad to do so if it had the same means of raising money that you fellows have," McCoy replied.

"What way do you think we have," demanded the mayor.

"You can tax them, we just have to ask them for it," McCoy shot back.

The mayor offered to donate a hangar and asked others to join him. When nobody did he said he would donate a hangar anyway (estimated to cost $150). [101]

A few days later, Kiggins was joined by Walter E. Carter, the owner of the popular CC Store, in donating $150 for construction of a hangar. The two donated hangars were completed in November. That donated by Kiggins was occupied by Dick Rankin. Rankin kept his instruction ship in the hangar and had his office next to it. The Carter hangar was occupied by a plane from the Adcox school in Portland. A third hangar, larger than the other two, was being built for a Stinson *Detroiter* owned by Harrey K. Coffey of Portland. (The *Detroiter* was the first American plane to incorporate in its design an entirely enclosed cabin with soundproofing and heat, engine starter,

and brakes on the wheels.) This hangar was to rent for $20 a month, the others for $15 a month. The hangars were of frame construction with a composition roof and sliding doors. [102]

Councilman Henry Rasmussen, as head of the aviation committee, appointed Barry Raguse, a city police officer, as municipal airport manager. Raguse, it was said, would enforce the state and federal Department of Commerce air rules. This move was lauded by E. E. Mouton, Commerce's supervisor for eight states, and Wilbur Wright, the department's aeronautical inspector at Portland. Mouton characterized Washington state as a "mecca" for incompetent aircraft operators and commended Vancouver's "progressive movement in protecting the public." [103]

At a council meeting November 18th an airport fund was created to make the handling of airport finances easier. The airport itself was discussed when Councilman Vyrett Chamberlain suggested the city take over Lamka's contract to purchase approximately four acres north of the municipal field. Rasmussen objected to such a course because no long-term agreement had been reached with the railroad regarding the 72 acres which comprised most of the commercial field. [104]

The *Columbian* criticized the council's handling of the airport in reporting on the December 2 meeting. A headline read: "Problem of Aviation Field Pops Up Again but City Fathers Do Nothing." It was reported that Rasmussen had a group of businessmen interested in building 10 to 12 new hangars, but the councilman thought the "celebrated" four acres under contract to Lamka should be acquired before the hangars were built. (The four acres were desirable because they were higher than much of the field and thus would be less endangered by high water from the Columbia River. Parts of the field were subject to flooding before the Bonneville Dam was completed in 1937. Even after this the field was occasionally flooded.)

The paper reminded readers that the "troublesome matter of the railroad lease on the main 72 acres" had not been resolved. The story concluded sarcastically that the "officials finally threatened to see somebody about the whole affair and went on." But just a few days later the mayor announced that he had reached a verbal agreement with the railroad for a five-year lease not to exceed $100 a month.[105]

The tone of the year's final council meeting was optimistic. The story was headlined: "Council Favors Rapid Expansion at Flying Field." Rasmussen said that construction of 10 hangars would begin that week. There would be eight more 36-foot hangars which housed "one of the common type of airplane used in student and passenger work." Two 50-foot hangars were to be constructed for cabin planes. Rasmussen estimated the cost of the 10 hangars at less than $150 each, unpainted. The Vancouver Plywood Company had volunteered to provide labor for the construction "at cost." Companies providing the materials showed "their civic spirit by agreeing to wait for their pay." It was felt that the hangars would pay for themselves in 10 months (renting at $15 a month).

Additional revenue from existing hangars, a shop, lunch counter, "and so forth" would help defray the $100 a month lease payments. There was also talk of taking over the space the city leased to Kong Loy (who farmed the acreage) at the east end of the field. The possibility of Aircraft Builders, Inc. (builders of Student Prince airplanes) of Portland locating a factory at the field was discussed. The company did locate "temporarily" in the old Sandifer shipyards (west of the Interstate Bridge). The Student Prince airplanes were, at least, tested at the Vancouver field as well as other local fields.[106]

The optimistic tone continued into the new year. A story on January 2 was bullish on the airport: "with hangar after hangar rising in a row at the municipal airport, the field is fast coming to look like a busy airport instead of a mere landing field." Of course, this was happening around the country as aviation grew and required more

facilities to meet the demands placed on it. It was reported that there were a total of seven hangars on the field and a shop building which could also house a plane. One of the hangars could house two craft so the hangar capacity was nine planes. Five of the hangars had been constructed under the auspices of the city, three of these were of larger dimensions (50-foot width), and able to house a cabin plane. Much of the preparation of the hangar sites, it was reported, was done by prisoners from the city jail "so that the expense is being kept to a minimum."[107]

Lamka resigned from the council at its first meeting of the year. He said he was "unable to attend meetings" and cited "adverse circumstances and conditions" as reasons for his resignation. It was accepted without comment.[108]

It was announced at the same session that the city and the S.P.&S. Railroad had signed a five-year lease for the 72 acres. The lease started December 1, 1929, and did not have the usual clause allowing the lessor to terminate the lease on 30 days notice, thus providing the city and its airport with a more stable future. As the acreage included grounds to the east and north of the airport "proper" it also provided frontage on Fifth Street and high ground for hangars, features thought previously to be available only on the four acres under contract to Lamka.

The recently created airport fund was abolished on the advice of state examiners and the funds transferred to the general fund. It was decided not to renew Kong Loy's sub-lease on the land he was farming at the east end of the field. When his lease expired the fences on the lot were removed and the area levelled. This enlargement in the field would give it a higher government rating and, it was hoped, make it "even more popular with aviators."[109]

Hopes for an airplane factory on the field continued into 1930 as well. Councilman Rasmussen, head of aviation committee, reported on a proposed contract between the city and the First National Flying System. The city would purchase

The "Flying Bathtub," a local experimental.   (Horace Sharon photo)

(Horace Sharon photo)   *Stearman* Speed Mail.

Clarence Murray's OX-5 powered American Eagle.

(Horace Sharon photo)

Bookwalter's "City of Vancouver" after crashing in southern Oregon during a National Air Derby race.

(Walt Bohrer photo)

the four acres which had been under contract to Lamka for $4,000, making semi-annual payments of $300. The city would build, within 90 days of demand, a factory building on the acreage, provided that the company pay $2,000 representing the last 20 months' payments on a five-year lease. The company would be tax-free except for fixtures and personal property. It would receive unlimited free use of the field.

Though the council expressed enthusiasm for the chance of having the factory, reservations were expressed concerning the free use of the field and the provision binding the city to build on demand. The matter was referred back to the aviation committee. An ordinance authorizing a $4,000 emergency warrant for labor, construction materials, and insurance at the airport was approved.[110]

The work at the airport had "materially altered" its appearance the *Columbian* reported. Eleven new hangars had been erected including a 50-foot hangar donated by the Vancouver Plywood Company. This hangar attracted special notice due to the walls and doors being of specially finished plywood. The grain of the wood was visible through a "silvery coating" which produced a "distinctive effect." The *Columbian* called it the "prize hangar" on the field. It was occupied by the mail plane of the Breese Aircraft Company of Portland. A lane leading into the airport and the taxi lane were graded, graveled, and rolled, and a fence along the east end of the field was removed along with some boulders. In April, electric lights were installed in the hangars. It was also planned to place four arc lights (like street lights) along the hangars. Though night flying was not anticipated, it was thought that the lights could save lives should an emergency arise.[111]

All of this work and the subsequent oiling of the roadway and taxi lane and the filling of depressions on the field moved the *Columbian* to observe at the end of April that the appearance of the airport was now "vastly altered." At the same time Arnold Peik, Herman Hendricks, and William Leibenstrett obtained a building permit to construct a motor repair shop at the field. The Interstate Machine Shop was the first airplane motor repair shop in Southwest Washington. J. L. "Dad" Bacon, who specialized in wing and fuselage repair, was reported to be outgrowing his quarters at the field.[112]

The field's hangars were painted in June. It was anticipated that two more would be constructed in July. Later, manager Rafferty had shrubs and perennial flowers planted. More filling took place in December. This time it was to eliminate an old road which was considered "a distinct menace."[113]

The airway in the Columbia River Gorge was being improved as well. Beacons were placed on Wind Mountain and Beacon Rock and at Wauna Lake and the "Sweeny Place" (location unknown) during 1930. The beacons were turned on in early 1931.[114]

The physical changes at the airport were accompanied by an increase in community awareness of aviation. When the Vancouver Bus Company expressed its willingness to stop at the airport hangars on its East Vancouver route Councilman Rasmussen was enthusiastic. Not only would it facilitate access to the field by the growing number of aviators, but he thought it would also give other bus riders "a daily opportunity to become air-minded" and to see the development at the airport.

Lieutenant Carlton Bond, the field commander, hosted a scout troop interested in parachutes. Bond also led six Army planes (three from Pearson and three from Sand Point Field) in a flight over Mt. Hood which was filmed from one of Tex Rankin's planes for newsreel footage. Mayor Kiggins almost got "air-minded" himself after being invited to the dedication of a new administration building at Boeing Field by Seattle Mayor Frank Edwards. The invitation was dropped from a plane flying over the local airport, and Vance Breese volunteered to fly the mayor to Seattle. The mayor, however, did not take the flight.

Later in the month Al Greenwood piloted Ernest Christensen's *Eaglerock* biplane to 7,200 feet with photographer Paul Schulz and *Columbian* reporter Ray Bachman aboard. The trio went up to view a solar eclipse. Vance Breese impressed chamber members and city officials by putting his transport plane through a series of stunts. Breese, a mail and transport pilot, was performing the maneuvers for Department of Commerce inspectors to get his plane certified as airworthy.

The Chief of the Air Service, Major General J. E. Fechet, visited the field with Captain Ira Eaker and Lieutenant E. R. Quesada. In addition to Fechet, a Loeing amphibian biplane was also at the field.[115]

The chamber hosted a luncheon for 20 local aviators. After lunch the attendees were invited to go with the aviators to see the airport. The biggest attraction at both the luncheon and the airport was Mrs. Edith Foltz. Besides talking at the luncheon, the *Columbian* promised that Foltz would fly her *Eaglerock* biplane and "show the 'doubting Thomases' that there is nothing a modern girl can't do." Foltz was already an accomplished pilot. She was one of the few women in the country to hold a transport license. She also had taken second place in the women's National Air Races in 1929, as she would again in 1932. During World War II she transported aircraft to England.

Foltz was slated as the star of the upcoming dedication of the municipal field and was chosen to preside as queen. The main event of this formal opening of the airport was an "air carnival."

To alert the public, the S.P.&S. band and Elks Club Drum Corps led a parade through Vancouver's business district. The parade included an Alexander glider and a tiny Heath parasol plane. In addition, Clarence Murray flew his American *Eagle* biplane over local communities and dropped handbills from the air. Murray and the band also went to the nearby towns of Ridgefield, La Center, Kalama, Kelso, Longview, Camas, and Washougal.

The dedication was held on May 25 with a crowd estimated at 10,000. Among the many fliers at the air carnival, Vance Breese and "Hap" Roundtree received special notice for their stunts. Clarence Murray was flying again, this time in an Alexander glider. J. C. Graul, chief pilot for Art Whitaker's Paramount Flying School, finally got Mayor Kiggins aloft to drop a dedicatory wreath on the field. Edith Foltz was, as billed, the star of the show. She took Councilman Rasmussen, who had directed many of the airport improvements, for his first airplane ride. She also won the dead-stick (i.e. engine off) landing contest. Foltz stopped her plane "almost squarely on the finish line and many yards closer than any of her male competitors." Those organizing the dedication were said to have been "more than satisfied."[116]

In July, Varney Airlines appointed Mrs. Ethel Wood as its official representative in Vancouver. She also acted as an agent for Pacific Air Transport, giving out schedules, fares, and such. As Varney and Pacific Air Transport were two of the five airlines that would form United Airlines, Wood's acting for both airlines presaged the industry giant's eventual formation.

Varney used the municipal field to conduct training in blind flying. A Stearman *Speed Mail* used for the instruction, was modified with frosted celluloid placed over the front cockpit. Another pilot rode in the rear cockpit in case of emergency. During a demonstration a pilot took off and landed several times, flew up the Columbia River Gorge, and even pulled the plane out of a spin on instruments. The blind flying instruction was to increase the safety of mail pilots flying in clouds or fog.[117]

The first Pacific Northwest Air Tour used the Vancouver Municipal Airport as its starting point. The tour was to cover 1765 miles and visit 22 cities. Three fliers from Vancouver took part in the tour (which was sponsored by the National Aeronautical Association): Edith Foltz, Al Greenwood, and Joe Cox. Those taking part intended to demonstrate the feasibility of flying under all conditions. The city leased the airport to the tour for the day of July 29, 1930.

About half of the 49 ships slated to take part in the tour put on an exhibition during the morning. Tex and Dick Rankin, Dorothy Hester, Foltz, Gordon Mounce, and Maurice King were among the better known fliers taking part in the exhibition.

A large crowd gathered for the program which included a triple parachute jump by Frank Brooks and outside loops by Hester. The *Columbian* bragged that the tour's aviators praised the field in "unstinted fashion."[118]

Vance Breese's custom Breese (Horace Sharon photo)
Monoplane. *Breese had been a demonstration pilot on the Ryan M-1.*

Student Prince manufactured planes (Horace Sharon photo)
locally and tested many of them at Pearson Field.

This Stinson Detroiter *is fitted with a* (Horace Sharon photo)
165 hp Wright engine.

*The Vancouver Municipal
Airport in 1930.*

(Horace Sharon photo)

Ford Trimotor dwarfs a Monocoupe at the field, September 1928. (Clark County Historical Museum)

Barling NB-3 with Armstrong-Siddely Genet *engine.*

(Horace Sharon photo)

Ernie Christiansen, L.C. ''Hap'' Roundtree, and Al Greenwood with an Alexander Eaglerock on Vancouver's commercial field ca. 1930. The Eaglerock was a popular private aircraft. (Pearson Air Museum/Art Whitaker photo)

Carlton Bond

Capt. Carlton Bond, who commanded Pearson Field from 1929 to 1933, and again 1938 to 1940, was a veteran of the Mexican Campaign. He joined the Army in 1916 and was sent to help chase bandits along the Mexican border. During World War I he took flight training in one of the first cadet classes in what was then the aviation section of the Army Signal Corps and was commissioned a second lieutenant.

Forsaking fixed wing aircraft, he entered the international balloon races in Geneva, Switzerland during the early 1920s.

Bond took over command of the 321st Observation Squadron from Aubrey Eagle in 1929 and remained in command until August, 1933. He was a good administrator as well as a top pilot. He was responsible for moving the old Spruce Production office to the east end of the field where both it and the old hangar still stand.

He was later assigned to serve at a number of other airfields around the world. He retired with the rank of colonel Jan. 5, 1948, and returned to his home in Vancouver where he died Feb. 5, 1980.

(Troy Wayrynen photo)

Leah Hing

Leah Hing, receptionist at the Oregon Aero Club, won acclaim 62 years ago as the first Chinese-American woman to earn a pilot's license. Leah, born and reared in the United States, was a mild mannered 24-year old debutante in 1931, but when the Japanese attacked China, Leah was outraged at the atrocities committed by the Japanese against her homeland.

She tried to volunteer for duty in the Chinese Army. Then she decided to volunteer for the Chinese Air Force. Tex Rankin, famous flier of the day, and Pat Reynolds, a reserve officer in the Army at Pearson Field, taught her to fly. She never got to China, but she still cherishes that first pilot certificate — No. 2741.

In 1938 she wrecked her Fleet biplane when she struck a mudhole while landing on Pearson Field, but escaped uninjured. When World War II broke out and all aircraft in Western Oregon were grounded, Hing sold her plane and hung up her wings. Now, at 85, she is still active in the Chinese community and in aviation circles.

The Consolidated PT-1's that the 321st Observation Squadron used in the late 1920's. The planes looked as if they were partly dismantled because the engine cowlings were removed for better cooling. A Douglas 0-2 is at right.

(Clark County Historical Museum)

CHAPTER IX

ARMY RECEIVES UPGRADED EQUIPMENT
"Much Needed New Planes Help in Search and Rescue Missions"

The Army upgraded its flying equipment in June 1930. Consolidated PT-3A's replaced the PT-1's. The new ships were powered by air-cooled Wright J-5 engines. The PT-1's were equipped with water-cooled Wright E's. The old ships' cowlings weren't used, the result being, according to the *Columbian*, that it "made them look always to the uninitiated as if they were about to come apart." Probably more important than the improved aesthetics of the PT-3A's was that they had 30 more horsepower (210 hp) than the older ships. They were reported to cruise at 75 m.p.h. while the PT-1's "seldom cruised above 70."[119]

In contrast to these training planes were some visiting Boeing P-12C pursuit craft. Three lieutenants stopped at Pearson on their way to Selfridge Field (Michigan) from the Boeing plant in Seattle. The P-12C's cruised at 135 m.p.h. and topped out at 170 m.p.h. They reportedly made a high speed dive over Vancouver at 280 m.p.h. It was not unusual for pilots ferrying aircraft to stop at Pearson. This underlined the importance of intermediate landing fields to the Air Corps' national airways.[120]

The fliers of the 321st started the new year (1931) by searching for a missing mail pilot. J. Russell Cunningham had radioed on January 1 that he was going down in sleet and fog in southern Oregon (Douglas County). The next day Carlton Bond led four ships from Pearson to the search area. Bad weather made the aerial search ineffective. Cunningham walked out to a ranch on the 2nd. Ice on the wings had forced him down.[121]

Twenty days later the reserve airmen were again searching for a missing mail pilot. Bond, flying a Douglas O-2H, accompanied by four other Army planes from Pearson, flew to Rufus, Oregon. Seven National Guard craft from Spokane joined the wide ranging search for Walter Case. Case, a pilot with Varney Airlines, disappeared while making an eastbound mail flight out of Swan Island. His destination had been Pasco. Fog and low clouds hampered the search which included the Army planes, Varney ships and other civilian craft, and ground parties. Searches centered around Stevenson, Goldendale, Odessa (70 miles southwest of Spokane), and Mt. Adams in Washington. In Oregon the search ranged from Bend to Sandy.

The wreck of Case's plane was finally spotted by another Varney pilot, Al Davis, while flying the same mail run on which Case had crashed. Davis had promised Case's wife that he would find him. Ground parties reached the crash site, located on the saddle between Silver Star and Little Baldy Mountains (in Skamania County northeast of Vancouver), after a grueling hike through the snow. Case had apparently been killed instantly on impact.[122]

The same day (January 29) on which the *Columbian* reported the Case wreck found, it also reported on the death of Fred Sauer, a Rankin instructor and Vancouver field regular. Sauer and a student had been practicing spins above the Columbia River when they failed to pull out of one in time. The student survived but Sauer drowned, probably due to the weight of his parachute and flying suit. Several planes from Vancouver, including all of Art Whitaker's Paramount Flying Service craft, flew to Kalama, Washington for Sauer's funeral.[123]

Lieutenant Bond assisted a United States Geological Survey project during February and March. Two geologists had snowshoed in to Skookum Meadows along the North Fork of the Lewis River. They were to monitor the river's flow as part of a survey of the Columbia River and its tributaries. Bond would fly supplies to a predetermined spot where he would drop them. The bundles were "partially protected" by a "thick wrapping of old Columbians." Bond would return two days later to check if the geologists had received their supplies. If they had, they would mark a "huge O.K." in the snow. This was another example of how the airplane was changing the way people did things.[124]

During May 1931, the Air Corps conducted a massive exercise at Dayton, Ohio. Some 667 planes from all over the country converged at Dayton. Following these exercises the 20th Pursuit Group's return to its base at Mather Field (Sacramento, California) brought it to Pearson Field. The Columbian noted, "These will be no ordinary aircraft. Most of them will be those lightning-fast Boeing singe-seat fighters whose waspish roar has been heard over Vancouver at intervals as they winged southward from the factory at Seattle. Besides the swift pursuit ships will be the slower, ponderous transports carrying the mechanics and equipment needed to keep the armada in flying trim."[125]

Weather delayed the Group's arrival at Vancouver several times. On June 9 six transports flew in from Spokane. The pursuits had attempted to fly to Seattle but weather conditions forced them to turn back. The transports consisted of two Ford trimotors, a Fokker trimotor, two single engine Fokkers, and a single engine Douglas biplane. There was also a Curtiss Condor bomber which was heading for Spokane with a spare engine for one of the P-12's.

Thirty-six of the pursuit planes flew in to Pearson on the 10th. They had by-passed Seattle and flown down the Columbia River Gorge. The Columbian asserted, as it often did, the superiority of the Columbia River Gorge airway and its logical termination at Vancouver. Arriving in an impressive "V" formation the two squadrons separated, one flying over Portland and the other over Vancouver. The ships landed on the field in disciplined threes and sixes.

Also visiting was what the Columbian called a "queer-shaped bomber." It was a Boeing prototype, an XB-9. Piloting the ship was Major Erik Nelson of Round-the-World fame. The paper rightly noted it was of "radical new design." None of the local aviators had seen such a plane. It was of all-metal construction with low cantilever wings and retractable landing gear. Nearly as fast as a pursuit ship, many of the B-9's innovations were later incorporated into Boeing's Model 247 airliner. The Columbian said that "it looked like little more than a flying wing while in the air."

The fliers spent the night at Vancouver and were entertained at a stag dinner at the Evergreen Hotel. They left the next morning to appear at Tacoma and Seattle. The fliers returned in late afternoon to again stay overnight.

When the two squadrons took off in the morning they put on an impressive display of formation flying. As the 77th squadron "passed back and forth overhead the watchers below marvelled repeatedly at the geometric precision of their formations, among them a straight line, a great 'V', and lastly their squadron number, written in the sky in a perfect '77' travelling at more than 100 miles an hour." The 20th Pursuit Group returned to Pearson Field the following June.[126]

Boeing P-12 of the 20th Pursuit Group on a visit to Pearson Field. The card insignia consists of two aces with a seven on either side, signifying the 77th Squadron, one of three that made up the Group.

(Pearson Air Museum)

1931: 20th Pursuit Group Boeing P-12 at Pearson Field. The significance of the swastika insignia remains a mystery.

(Pearson Air Museum)

Douglas BT-2A in front of the 1921 hangar that still stands on the field.

(Pearson Air Museum)

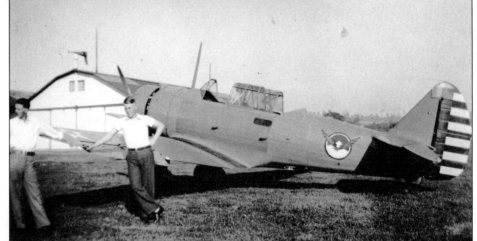

The 321st Observation Squadron gets its first monoplane. This BT-9 came to the squadron in the 1930s.

(Clark County Historical Museum)

BT-9 with PT-3 in background.

(Clark County Historical Museum)

Field commander Lt.
Carlton Bond with friend,
ca. 1929.

(Clark County Historical Museum)

Boeing XB-9 at the field,
1931.

(Horace Sharon photo)

The Army was ordered to
fly the mail in 1934.
These Douglas O-25's
operated out of Pearson.

(Horace Sharon photo)

Early in 1934, President Franklin Roosevelt cancelled the air mail contracts. He charged that the previous Republican administration and the carriers had engaged in fraud and collusion in the awarding of the contracts. On February 9th, the Air Corps was ordered to fly the mail.

The following day the *Columbian* reported that Pearson Field might serve as an air mail center and that reserve fliers had been told to be ready to fly the mail. The Chamber of Commerce Aviation Committee was excited by the prospect of having the field designated as an air mail center. J. L. "Dad" Bacon had crews install carbide lights to make the field suitable for night landings. One of the four Douglas B-7's at the field made a night landing and the pilot declared the lighting adequate. (This cooperation between civilians on the municipal field and military authorities on Pearson Field is an example of the difficulty of considering the two fields as separate entities.)

It became clear however that the air mail center would remain at Swan Island Airport. Pearson Field would serve as Air Corps headquarters and provide maintenance and hangar space. The field would be used when weather rendered Swan Island unusable. The Air Corps mail operation took over the two Army hangars and the administration building. The 321st was left with one office. Twenty-eight enlisted men and 25 civilian worked maintaining the planes.

Nine Douglas O-25's were stationed at Pearson to fly the mail. The front cockpits were modified at "Dad" Bacon's shop to serve as mail compartments. The mail was flown on two routes: Portland - Salt Lake City and Seattle - Portland - Boise. Between February 12th and early May, the Army pilots carried 43,179 pounds of mail and flew 194,140 miles of a scheduled 201,326 miles, or about 97 percent. There were no serious mishaps or lost or damaged mail.

Elsewhere the Air Corps' experience was not so good. A number of serious accidents, several of them fatal, marred the Corps' reputation. The Baker Board was appointed to investigate the con-

duct of the Air Corps. The Army fliers were hardly to blame. They had been told to carry the mail during the winter months with its dangerous weather. Their training was applicable to military situations, not the night and all-weather flying over set routes that was required in flying mail. Air Corps equipment was not designed to carry freight, nor equipped with navigational aids.

There was fallout for the aviation industry as well. Besides the severe economic jolt, many aviation pioneers, including United Airlines' first president, Philip Johnson, were blackballed from the industry. The charges of collusion were never proven. United was eventually awarded $364,423 for losses incurred as a result of the air mail contract cancellation. The President had badly disrupted the industry by cancelling the contracts.[127]

As the Great Depression and the 1930s wore on, the activities at Pearson Field and the municipal airport remained much the same as in the previous years. The reserve pilots flew on the weekends and civilian pilots took to the air when they could. And in 1937, the glare of international attention was felt at the field when the first non-stop flight over the North Pole landed there.

In 1938, a new airport was completed across the Columbia River in Portland. The expanded version of this airport is today's Portland International Airport. When war came in late 1941, Vancouver Barracks took on a busy character. For security reasons, civilian flying was banned along the Pacific Coast and Vancouver's municipal airport was closed for the duration of the war. The Army's Pearson Field became a parking lot, covered with trucks and jeeps. (Though Danny Grecco said that a gravel emergency strip was maintained.) During the war the older of the Army's two hangars (the one that still stands today) became a barracks for Italian prisoners of war.[128]

After the war the field returned to its prewar activity. With the much larger Portland Airport available, the Army, in the tradition of post-war downsizing, decided that it no longer required Pearson Field. Still, the War Assets Administration realized that the field was important to the area's aviation. In 1949, through a quit claim deed, Pearson Field (now the portion of Pearson Airpark west of East Reserve Street) was given to the city of Vancouver. The Army thought it wise, however, to retain avigation rights to the field.

Pearson Airpark in the 1960s. (Clark County Historical Museum)

Marvin Joy designed and built this "flying fuselage" without real wings or ailerons, in the late 1930s. Joy was a bridge tender on the railroad bridge over the Columbia River slough. Danny Grecco test flew the plane on a brief circuit around the area, then landed without incident, according to Lowell Moore who saw the flight. Later, after Joy had modified the plane again, Sid Monastes took off for a test flight. He got off the ground, then lost altitude, hooked its tail over the barbed wire at the east end of the runway and turned a full somersault, landing on the gear, neatly wrapped in barbed wire but suffering only minor injuries. That was the end of what reporter Lev Richards dubbed the flying flapjack. J.B. Dobson, manager of the Pendleton Woolen Mills and a colonel in the Air National Guard invested heavily to finance the various versions of the flapjack.

(Lev Richards photos)

Spartan C-3 with Wright Whirlwind engine sports a Texaco logo. The company probably supplied a monthly stipend of gas and oil for this flying advertisement.

(Horace Sharon photo)

Boeing P-26 ''Peashooter.''

(Horace Sharon photo)

91

Don Blair

Don Blair learned to fly in self defense. "We lived across the road from the site of Evergreen Field. Sid Monastes used to buzz me in his Eaglerock when I was walking home from school on Mill Plain," Don recalled. "So I took lessons from Don Coffield and Art Severson in a Taylorcraft and Waco F-2 and won my 2-S rating in 1938." He has been flying ever since, piling up about 8,000 hours in the next 50 years. He answered the call for flight instructors during World War II, then taught ground school for B-29 crews at the Boeing plant in Seattle.

When World War II ended Don turned to flying the bush in Alaska in 1951 and 1952. He has some scary stories to tell of those days. He returned to Vancouver to fly for the Washington State Game Department and established his own flight school and charter service in the old wooden hangar on Pearson Field for five years. He also flew a Fairchild 24 aerial mapping plane shooting pictures for Crown Zellerbach and other customers.

Don is an active member of the Pearson Air Museum and spent long hours helping to establish the museum. He is still active in the museum, the OX-5 Club, the Aviation Breakfast Club in Portland and anything else involving flying.

Lowell Moore

Lowell Moore, 79, is a walking encyclopedia of aviation. He sees all, hears all, knows all about the early days in the Vancouver-Portland area. He used to haunt J. L. Bacon's Pearson Field shop 60 years ago as a boy on a bicycle. He was graduated from high school in 1933. He and Edgar Davis (Smith) earned their A&E (aircraft and engine) licenses in 1933 in Dad Bacon's school. They soon took over the flight line, pumping gas and servicing aircraft from 1935 to 1937. Then Lowell went to work for Columbia Aircraft Industries in Portland, making parts for B24s, PBYs and BT-13s.

He took a few lessons and did a lot of flying with other pilots, but never got his own pilot's license. He flew with Don Coffield on the first Oregon Air Tours in 1937 and 1939, and sold tickets for Coffield on barnstorming forays.

Moore was admitted to the OX-5 Club in 1959 and served as secretary-treasurer for years, and president twice. He is still active in OX-5 and conducts tours of the Air Museum where some of his pictures of the early days are on display.

(Lowell Moore photo)

A 321st Observation Squadron training flight over Mt. Hood. (Clark County Historical Museum)

Pearson Airpark has served for many years as a regional general aviation airport and continues to do so as of this writing. But the future of the airport is clouded. Ironically this historic airport is threatened with closure by an adjacent historic site.

Vancouver has always been proud of its history. The city can trace its origins to the winter of 1824-25 when the Hudson's Bay Company, a British fur trading concern, built an outpost on a bluff near the present site of the Washington State School for the Deaf. A few years later, during the winter of 1828-29, the company constructed a new stockade on the flats closer to the Columbia River. This new location would later be part of Vancouver Barracks and Pearson Field.

Fort Vancouver, as it was known, served as the company's headquarters for a vast region in the Pacific Northwest. Its location, on the north side of the Columbia River, was an attempt to strengthen British claims to the region. The Treaty of 1846, however, set the boundary between the United States and Britain's holdings at the 49th parallel, far north of the Columbia. Three years later, on May 13, 1849, the United States Army arrived at Fort Vancouver and established a post. The Hudson's Bay Company's activities wound down with the company abandoning Fort Vancouver in 1860.

Over the years the citizens of Vancouver made efforts to commemorate this part of their heritage. It will be recalled that in 1925, as part of the celebration of the fort's centennial, that Lieutenant Oakley Kelly made a record-breaking flight from Vancouver to San Francisco to retrieve commemorative coins minted there. Various efforts were made to locate the old fort site and many hoped to build a replica of the stockade.

The efforts of local groups, especially the Fort Vancouver Historical and Restoration Society, resulted in the establishment of the Fort Vancouver National Monument on June 19, 1948. With continued lobbying by local citizens brought a redesignation of the monument as the Fort Vancouver

National Historic Site on June 30, 1961. The National Park Service was charged with the administration of the site.

Archaeological work and archival research made possible the determination of the fort's actual historic location. In 1966 work began on the construction of a replica of the old fort. Over several years the stockade, bastion, and a few of the buildings have been completed.

In order for the stockade walls to be constructed the Vancouver Aviation Advisory Committee and the city of Vancouver gave permission for the intrusion into Pearson Airpark's airspace. The airpark also gave up use of its cross-wind runway that ran roughly north-south near the site of the reconstruction.

In 1972 the ownership of the western half of Pearson Airpark went to the National Park Service in a three-way land deal that also involved the city of Vancouver and the S. P. & S. Railroad. The city was given a lease that ran until 2002 at the rate of one dollar per year. There is disagreement among the parties which negotiated the agreement whether it was intended that aviation use end in 2002.

The issue re-emerged with the formation of the Pearson Airpark Historical Society in 1985. The immediate cause of the founding of the society were discussions held between the city of Vancouver and the Portland Trailblazers, a professional basketball franchise in Portland, Oregon, regarding the possibility of building a sports facility on Pearson Airpark.

The all-volunteer society dedicated itself to preserving the airpark's history and maintaining the historic activity at the airpark: flying airplanes. The substantial public support the society gathered caused the city of Vancouver to re-think its position on the airpark. Subsequently, the city became one of the most enthusiastic advocates of Pearson Airpark's preservation.

In 1988 the Pearson Airpark Historical Society opened the Pearson Air Museum in one of the city-owned hangars. In addition to exhibits on the history of the field, the museum displayed several antique aircraft. The aircraft were privately owned and all were flown at least seasonally by their owners. To expose the public to the widest array of planes possible, the museum rotated the aircraft on display.

The National Park Service had other plans for the western half of the airpark. It planned to forbid aviation on that portion of the airpark after the lease expired in 2002. The land would be cleared and potatoes and other crops planted to complement the replica of Fort Vancouver. The Service maintained that aviation interfered with the 1840s theme at the fort site.

Airpark proponents pointed out that there were many other modern intrusions: the nearby Portland International Airport, an adjacent highway, and a nearby freeway and railroad, and the general urban character of the area. The Pearson Airpark Historical Society and the city of Vancouver offered a series of compromises which involved varying plans to remove modern buildings from the western half of the airpark and minimize the perceived impact of the airpark on the fort site through the use of berms and plant buffers. The National Park Service rejected all of these efforts.

In recognition of the need to resolve the dispute the area's congresswoman, Jolene Unsoeld, introduced a bill in the United State Congress to create a Vancouver National Historic Reserve Study Commission. The commission would consider alternatives for a comprehensive management of several contiguous areas of historical and cultural significance. These were Vancouver Barracks, Officers' Row, the Fort Vancouver National Historic Site, the former Kaiser Shipyards site, parts of the Columbia River waterfront, and Pearson Airpark. The future of Pearson Airpark figured large in the work of the commission. After studying the alternatives, the commission would make recommendations to Congress.

Congresswoman Unsoeld's bill was passed and a five-member commission was appointed.

The commission members represented the governmental units which were property holders within the proposed reserve. None of the commission members had expertise in aviation matters.[129]

The commission held a series of public meetings and hearings over a period of nearly two years. The testimony to the commission and the debate among its members was sometimes heated. In early 1993, the commission agreed upon a series of recommendations.

The commission recommended that a Vancouver National Historic Reserve be formed. To facilitate this, a Vancouver Partnership would be created consisting of the affected property owners and two representatives of the community at large. The National Park Service would be the lead agency in administering the Reserve. Cooperation would be encouraged through the use of memorandums of understanding, rather than inflexible federal legislation. The Partnership would develop a Reserve Coordination Master Plan that would outline the management of the Reserve. Pearson Airpark's future hinges on how these arrangements are carried out. As of June 1993, congress had not acted on the commission's recommendations.

1. This chapter is based on *Vancouver Columbian* [hereafter VC], 18, 19, 20, 21, 22, 23, 28 June 1937, 7, 10, 13, 14, 15, 16, 30 July 1937, 7 August 1937; *Portland Oregonian* [hereafter OR], 21, 22 June 1937; *New York Times*, 20, 21 June 1937; Von Hardesty, "Soviets Blaze Sky Trail Over Top of World," *Air and Space*, vol. 2, no. 5, (December 1987/January 1988): 48-54; Roy Jones, "Clark County Aviation," *Clark County History* (Vancouver, Washington: Fort Vancouver Historical Society, 1968), 313-315; Baidukov, Georgiy, *Russian Lindbergh: The Life of Valery Chkalov*, ed. VonHardesty, trans. Peter Belov, (Washington, D.C. and London: Smithsonian Press, 1991). Hardesty's introduction provides the reader with a sense of the context in which the flight took place. Katherine Tupper Marshall, *Together* (Chicago: Peoples Book Club, 1946, 1947) 25-28.

2. *Vancouver Independent*, 30 April 1890, 22 April 1891; *Vancouver Columbian* 26 June 1911.

3. *Vancouver Independent*, 21 September 1905; VC 28 September 1927; Patrick Harris, *The Coming of the Birdman: The Aviator's Image in Oregon 1905-1915* (Portland, Oregon: Masters Thesis, Portland State University, 1981), 21-32; Don Dwiggins, *The Air Devils* (Philadelphia and New York: J. B. Lippincott and Company, 1966), 103; Lester J. Maitland, *Knights of the Air* (Garden City, New York: Doubleday, Doran and Company, 1929), 132.

4. Roger E. Bilstein, *Flight in America* (Baltimore: The John Hopkins University Press, 1984), 17.

5. VC 2 March 1910; OR 6 March 1910; for more on Hamilton's flights in Portland see Harris, 56-63.

6. VC 16, 23 May 1911.

7. VC 23, 30 May 1911, 13, 15, 16, 21, 27, 30 June 1911, 27 July 1911, 5 August 1911, 4, 5, 7, October 1911; OR 16 June 1911; Harris, 74, 87-88. For more on the aviation activities of the Mannings see Harris, 54, 69-75.

8. VC 20, 23 May 1912, 7 June 1912; OR 22 June 1912; William Wagner, *Ryan, the Aviator* (New York: McGraw-Hill Book Company, 1971), 5-6.

9. OR 5, 17 June 1912.

10. OR 10 June 1912.

11. VC 12 June 1912; OR 10, 12 June 1912; Harris, 88-90.

12. OR 21 June 1912, 5 July 1912, 19 August 1912; Harris, 90.

13. VC 9, 10, 12 August 1912; OR 9, 10, 11 August 1912; Harris 90-91; Donald Dale Jackson, *Flying the Mail* (Alexandria, Virginia: Time-Life Books, 1982), 20.

14. VC 26 June 1915, 26 July 1915; OR 18 July 1915, 9 September 1917, 27 April 1947; Harris, 49-53; Roy Jones, "Clark County Aviation," *Clark County Historical Annual* (Vancouver, Washington: Fort Vancouver Historical Society, 1968), 305.

15. VC 2, 18 August 1917; OR 18 July 1915.

16. For a discussion of activity at Vancouver Barracks during World War I see Ted Van Arsdol, "World War I Brought Boom Times," *Clark County Historical Annual*, (Vancouver, Washington: Fort Vancouver Historical Society, 1976).

17. VC 8 February 1918.

18. For examples see VC 13, 14, 15, 20 August 1917.

19. Gordon B. Dodds, *The American Northwest, A History of Oregon and Washington* (Arlington Heights, Illinois: The Forum Press, Inc., 1986), 202-204.

20. VC 8 February 1918, 18 May 1918.

21. VC 18 May 1918, 21 November 1918, 4 December 1918, 29 November 1924; See also United States Army and United States Spruce Production Corporation, *History of Spruce Production Division*, n.d.

22. VC 7 February 1918, 21 March 1918, 20 April 1918, 23 August 1918, 13 November 1918, 14 February 1919; *History of Spruce Production Division.*

23. VC 21 November 1924.

24. VC 5 May 1919, 25, 27 August 1919, 1 September 1919, 5 September 1929.

25. VC 19 April 1921, 21 July 1921.

26. VC 22 May 1922, 2 June 1922, 12, 25 April 1923, 18 May 1923.

27. Jones, 306; VC 1 May 1923.

28. VC 25 April 1923; *The National Geographic Magazine* (Washington, D.C.: National Geographic Society, July 1924).

29. VC 25, 26, 27 July 1923.

30. VC 26 December 1923, 1 February 1924.

31. Earnest A. McKay, *A World to Conquer* (New York Arco Publishing, Inc., 1981), 5, 46.

32. VC 6, 11, 12, 17, 18, 19, 20, 26, 28, 29 March 1924.

33. VC 11, 12 April 1924.

34. VC 26 April 1924, 3, 8, 10 May 1924.

35. 23 June 1924, 8 July 1924.

36. VC 12 May 1924.

37. VC 30 June 1924, 22, 25, 27 August 1924, 1, 9, 11, 13, 22 September 1924, 22 November 1924, 31 July 1926, 16 September 1926.

38. VC 29 September 1924.

39. VC 17, 18 October 1924; McKay, 10-12.

40. VC 30 September 1924, 1, 13 October 1924.

41. VC 1, 3, 5 August 1925; Jones, 307; Maurer Maurer, *Aviation in the U.S. Army, 1919-1939* (Washington, D.C.: Office of Air Force History, United States Air Force, 1987), 142.

42. VC 15 October 1924, 20 November 1924, 5, 7, 9, 11 May 1925.

43. VC 23 October 1924, 1, 21, 26 November 1924, 23 December 1924, 23 April 1925, 20 March 1926.

44. McKay, 4.

45. Memo of 16 February 1925; VC 28 April 1925, 16, 17 September 1925.

46. VC 15, 16, 17 September 1925; OR 1 April 1923, 3 September 1924, 28 April 1925; Maurer, 28-32.

47. Carroll V. Glines, *Jimmy Doolittle: Daredevil Aviator and Scientist* (New York: The Macmillan Company, 1972), 85.

48. OR 13, 15, 17, 18 February 1921, 15 March 1921; Maurer, 177; *American Aviation Historical Society Journal* [hereafter AAHS] vol. 17, no. 4 (Winter 1972), 263-264.

49. Don Vorderman, *The Great Air Races* (Garden City, New York: Doubleday and Company, 1969), 98, 100; Thomas G. Foxworth, *The Speed Seekers* (New York: Doubleday and Company, 1975), 283-285.

50. VC 15 September 1925; OR 3 September 1924, 28 April 1925; Maurer, 172; AAHS, vol. 11, no. 1, 10; Maitland, 242; Foxworth, 223-224.

51. VC 27, 29, August 1925, 4, 5, 8, 10, 11, 12, 14, 15, 16, 17 September 1925; OR 17 September 1925; *Oregon Journal* 17 September 1925.

52. VC 27 April 1925.

53. 5, 9, 14, 16 May 1925.

54. 22, 28 May 1925.

55. Harris, 93; Wilbur H. Gorst, *Vern C. Gorst, Pioneer and Grandad of United Air Lines* (Coos Bay, Oregon: Gorst Publications, 1979). Frank J. Taylor, *High Horizons* (New York: McGraw Hill, 1962), 15-19.

56. VC 20, 22 March 1926.

57. MacKay, 4.

58. VC 22, 23 March 1926, 14, 20, 23, 26, 28, 31 July 1926.

59. VC 26 March 1926.

60. VC 16 April 1926; Jones, 318.

61. VC 5 April 1926.

62. VC 21 April 1926, 21 May 1926.

63. VC 29 April 1926, 1, 5, 11 May 1926.

64. VC 1, 21, 24 May 1926.

65. VC 13 September 1926.

66. VC 15 September 1926, 8 October 1926.

67. VC 14 September 1927.

68. VC 1, 20 April 1927, 7 July 1927, 3 September 1927, 10 October 1927.

69. VC 7, 8, 24 June 1927.

70. 16, 24 August 1927, 2, 12, 13, 14, 15, 16 September 1927.

71. Milton Bona, "Charles Lindbergh and Clark County", *Clark County History* (Vancouver, Washington: Fort Vancouver Historical Society, 1978), 33-37.

72. VC 29 January 1927, 21 July 1927, 24 September 1927, 15 November 1927.

73. VC 12 July 1927.

74. VC 1, 22, 23 April 1927, 10 October 1927.

75. VC 27 June 1927.

76. VC 18, 19 August 1927.

77. VC 25 August 1927, 20, 26, 27, 28 September 1927.

78. VC 28 September 1927.

79. VC 16, 17, 19, 21, 22, 23 September 1927; Walt Bohrer, *Black Cats and Outside Loops: Tex Rankin Aerobatic Ace* (Oregon City, Oregon: Plere Publishers, Inc., 1989), 112.

80. VC 3 December 1927.

81. VC 5 January 1928.

82. VC 21 January 1928.

83. VC 14, 22 March 1928.

84. VC 17 January 1928, 20 February 1928.

85. VC 27 April 1928, 15 May 1928, 12 June 1928.

86. VC 27 January 1928.

87. VC 3 March 1928, 8 June 1928.

88. VC 18, 19, 21 July 1928.

89. VC 28 April 1928.

90. VC 13 July 1928.

91. VC 27 September 1928, 8 October 1928, 21 January 1929.

92. VC 29 May 1928.

93. VC 28 April 1928, 21 May 1928, 20 November 1928.

94. VC 1 June 1929.

95. VC 18 June 1929, 6 August 1929.

96. VC 20 August 1929.

97. VC 24, 27, 28, June 1929, 1, 2, 3, 4 July 1929.

98. VC 22 June 1929, 6, 27, 29, 31 July 1929, 1, 5, 10, 12, 13, 15, 16, 17, 18 August 1929.

99. VC 26 July 1929, 3, 10, 14, 16, 19 September 1929, 8 February 1930, 3 June 1930.

100. VC 5, 14, 16, 18, 19 October 1929.

101. VC 22 October 1929.

102. VC 28 October 1929, 16 November 1929; Michael J. H. Taylor, ed., *Jane's Encyclopedia of Aviation* (London: Bestseller Publications Limited, 1989), 842.

103. VC 28 October 1929.

104. VC 19 November 1929.

105. VC 3, 6 December 1929.

106. VC 17 December 1929, 24 October 1930.

107. VC 2 January 1930.

108. VC 7 January 1930.

109. VC 7 January 1930.

110. VC 21 January 1930.

111. VC 21 February 1930, 14 March 1930, 9, 10 April 1930.

112. VC 14, 30 April 1930.

113. VC 12 June 1930, 9 July 1930, 21 November 1930, 1 December 1930.

114. VC 29 October 1930, 7 February 1931.

115. VC 21 February 1930, 8 March 1930, 11, 12, 14, 21, 28, 30 April 1930, 12 May 1930. Lt. (later Major) Carlton Bond was field commander 1929 to 1933 and again 1938 to 1940. Lt. (later Major) Paul E. Burrows was field commander 1933 to 1938. Lt. J. H. Cox filled that position 1940 until the field's closure (as an army field) about two years later.

116. VC 19, 21, 23, 24, 26 May 1930, 3 September 1932.

117. VC 3 June 1930, 26 July 1930.

118. VC 4, 18, 26, 28, 30 July 1930.

119. VC 11 June 1930.

120. VC 9 October 1930, for examples of P-12 visits see VC 4, 14, 27 February 1931.

121. VC 2, 3 January 1931.

122. VC 23, 24, 26, 27, 28, 29, 30 January 1931; Seth Davidson, *An Autobiography* (Washougal, Washington, n.d.), 59.

123. VC 29, 30 January 1931.

124. VC 28 February 1931, 13 March 1931.

125. VC 1 May 1931; Maurer, 246-248.

126. VC 1, 22, 23, 26, 28, 29 May 1931, 2, 3, 4, 5, 6, 8, 9, 10, 11, 12 June 1931, 28, 30 May 1932, 3, 7, 8, 9, 10, 11, 13, 14 June 1932.

127. VC 10, 13, 14, 15, 16, 17, 19 February 1934, 7, 10, 19 March 1934, 14 April 1934, 7 May 1934; Maurer, 308; Robert E. Johnson, *Airway One: A Narrative of United Airlines and its Leaders* (Chicago and Crawfordsville, Indiana: R. R. Donnelley and Sons, Company, 1974), 28-33.

128. For an overview of World War II in Vancouver see Ted Van Arsdol, "World War II in Vancouver," *Clark County History* (Vancouver, Washington: Fort Vancouver Historical Society, 1978), 5-32.

129. The commission members were: Dr. Harold A. Dengerink (Chairman) of Washington State University, Vancouver Campus, as representative of the general public; John Fishbach, City Manager, City of Vancouver, representative of the City of Vancouver; Horace H. Foxall, Jr., U.S. Army Corps of Engineers, representative of the Secretary of the Army; David M. Hansen, Washington State Deputy Historic Preservation Officer, representative of the Governor of Washington and the State Department of Archaeology and Historic Preservation; Charles H. Odegaard, Regional Director, Pacific Northwest Region, National Park Service, representative of the National Park Service. *Vancouver National Historical Reserve Feasibility Study and Environmental Assessment, Preliminary Final Report*, Vancouver Historical Reserve Study Commission (29 January 1993).

Information and quotes for all sidebars are drawn from the *Vancouver Columbian* and *Portland Oregonian*.

Baidukov, Georgiy. *Russian Lindbergh: The Life of Valery Chkalov.* Von Hardesty, ed., Peter S. Belov, trans. Washington, D.C. and London: Smithsonian Press, 1991.

Bilstein, Roger E. *Flight in America.* Baltimore: The John Hopkins University Press, 1984.

Bohrer, Walt. *Black Cats and Outside Loops: Tex Rankin Aerobatic Ace.* Oregon City: Plere Publishers, Inc., 1989.

Bona, Milton. "Charles Lindbergh and Clark County," *Clark County History.* Vancouver, Washington: Fort Vancouver Historical Society, 1978.

Davidson, Seth. *An Autobiography.* Washougal, Washington: Unpublished manuscript, n.d.

Dodds, Gordon B. *The American Northwest, A History of Oregon and Washington.* Arlington Heights, Illinois: The Forum Press, Inc., 1986.

Dwiggins, Don. *The Air Devils.* Philadelphia and New York: J.B. Lippincott and Company, 1966.

Foxworth, Thomas G. *The Speed Seekers.* New York: Doubleday and Company, 1975.

Glines, Carroll V. *Jimmy Doolittle: Daredevil Aviator and Scientist.* New York: The Macmillan Company, 1972.

Gorst, Wilbur H. *Vern C. Gorst, Pioneer and Grandad of United Air Lines.* Coos Bay, Oregon: Gorst Publications, 1979.

Hallion, Richard P., ed. *The Wright Brothers: Heirs of Prometheus.* Washington, D.C.: Smithsonian Institution, 1978.

Harris, Patrick John. *The Coming of the Birdman: The Aviator's Image in Oregon 1905-1915.* Masters Thesis, Portland State University, 1981.

Jackson, Donald Dale. *Flying the Mail.* Alexandria, Virginia: Time-Life Books, 1982.

Johnson, Robert E. *Airway One: A Narrative of United Airlines and its Leaders.* Chicago and Crawfordsville, Indiana: R.R. Donnelley and Sons, Company, 1974.

Jones, Roy. "Clark County Aviation", *Clark County History.* Vancouver, Washington: Fort Vancouver Historical Society, 1968.

Maitland, Lester J. *Knights of the Air.* Garden City, New York: Doubleday, Doran, and Company, Inc., 1929.

Maurer, Maurer. *Aviation in the U.S. Army, 1919-1939.* Washington, D.C.: Office of Air Force History, United States Air Force, 1987.

Marshall, Katherine Tupper. *Together.* Chicago: People's Book Club, 1946.

Marshall, Max L., ed. *The Story of the U.S. Army Signal Corps.* New York: Franklin Watts, Inc., 1965.

"Master Plan Report for Pearson Airpark". Corvallis, Oregon: Foresite Group, Inc., 1987.

McKay, Ernest A. *A World to Conquer.* New York: Arco Publishing, Inc., 1981.

Ogburn, Milton. *Wings of World War I.* New York: Exposition Press, 1970.

Shamburger, Page. *Tracks Across the Sky: The Story of the Pioneers of the U.S. Airmail.* Philadelphia and New York: J.B. Lippincott Company, 1964.

Taylor, Frank J. *High Horizons.* New York: McGraw-Hill, 1962.

Taylor, Michael J.H., ed. *Jane's Encyclopedia of Aviation.* London: Bestseller Publications Limited, 1989.

United States Army and United States Spruce Production Corporation. *History of Spruce Production Division.* n.d.

Van Arsdol, Ted. "World War I Brought Boom Times", *Clark County History.* Vancouver, Washington: Fort Vancouver Historical Society, 1976.

_____ "World War II in Vancouver." *Clark County History.* Vancouver, Washington: Fort Vancouver Historical Society, 1978.

Vancouver Historical Reserve Study Commission. *Vancouver National Historical Reserve Feasibility Study and Environmental Assessment, Preliminary Final Report.* 29 January 1993.

Vorderman, Don. *The Great Air Races.* Garden City, New York: Doubleday and Company, 1969.

Wagner, William. *Ryan, the Aviator.* New York: McGraw-Hill Book Company, 1971.

Newspapers:
The New York Times
The Oregonian (OR) Portland, Oregon.
The Oregon Journal Portland, Oregon.
Vancouver Columbian (VC) Vancouver, Washington.
Vancouver Independent (VI) Vancouver, Washington

Journals:
American Aviation Historical Society Journal

Magazines:

Hardesty, Von. "Soviets Blaze Sky Trail Over Top of World." *Air and Space,* vol. 2, no. 5 (December 1987/January 1988): 48-54.

The National Geographic Magazine. Washington, D.C.: National Geographic Society, vol. XCVI, no. 1 (July 1924).

Special thanks to the often unacknowledged recorders of twentieth century history — the photographers, families and institutions who preserve their collections.

Photography for this volume was drawn from:

Walt Bohrer, aviation historian
Clark County Historical Museum
Harold Kern
Dick Mitchell
Lowell Moore
National Air and Space Museum
National Archives
Oregon Historical Society
The Oregonian

Allan Peak
Pearson Air Museum
James Raley
Leverett Richards
Mrs. Clyde Ryan
Paul Schulz
Horace Sharon
Troy Wayrynen
Art Whitaker

(Allan Peak photos)